By *Theodora C. Stanwell-Fletcher*

DRIFTWOOD VALLEY
(*Awarded 1947 John Burroughs Medal*)

THE TUNDRA WORLD

THE TUNDRA WORLD

Parasitic jaegers chasing arctic tern across the summer tundra
by western Hudson Bay

THE TUNDRA WORLD

by Theodora C. Stanwell-Fletcher

FRONTISPIECE BY GEORGE MIKSCH SUTTON

AN ATLANTIC MONTHLY PRESS BOOK

LITTLE, BROWN AND COMPANY · BOSTON

LIBRARY OF CONGRESS CATALOG CARD NO. 52–6795

Published August 1952
Reprinted August 1952

ATLANTIC-LITTLE, BROWN BOOKS
ARE PUBLISHED BY
LITTLE, BROWN AND COMPANY
IN ASSOCIATION WITH
THE ATLANTIC MONTHLY PRESS

Published simultaneously
in Canada by McClelland and Stewart Limited

PRINTED IN THE UNITED STATES OF AMERICA

I have a liking for almost every kind of American. . . .
But there are two types which I value especially . . .
One is the pioneer . . . At his best, I think, I have found
him as a newcomer in Canada where he is pushing
North, pioneering in the old sense. By what signs is he
to be known? Principally by the fact that he is wholly
secure, that he possesses his soul, that he is the true
philosopher. He is one of the few aristocrats left in the
world. He has a right sense of the values of life because
his cosmos embraces both nature and man.

From *Pilgrim's Way* by LORD TWEEDSMUIR
Former Governor-General of Canada

Author's Note

᎒᎒᎒᎒᎒᎒᎒᎒᎒᎒᎒᎒᎒᎒᎒᎒᎒᎒᎒᎒᎒᎒

THE FIGURES in this book are all imaginary and are not intended to represent any actual persons. Their behavior and philosophies, the situations and natural environment, I have tried to make as accurate as possible. For these are based on my own observations and experiences during two summer seasons on the west coast of Hudson Bay; or on those of good friends who have lived there for many years, or taken extensive trips to study its wildlife. As in *Driftwood Valley*, I have made use again of the journal style because this seems to be an ideal form for expressing natural history observations. Accuracy in dates and timing, and freshness of detail, are important to naturalists.

The actual setting of this tale, which doesn't pretend at all to be a profound or detailed study, is that of a summer in the 1930's when I knew Churchill best and worked with fellow students on the plant and animal life of that region. In 1949 I stayed there again, and although this small subarctic settlement had grown considerably and become more conventionalized since the establishment of a military base there during World War II, its natural environment was exactly the same. So, also, was the profound conviction that man and his works are insignificant still against the bigness of the North.

Ten miles away by land or water there is still that primeval vastness of forest, sea, or arctic tundra. In the 1930's every person whom you met around Churchill seemed unusual or picturesque; now, amid elements brought in by the military camp and recent Arctic Research Station a few miles off, you must look harder to find them, but they are still there.

Wildlife immediately around Churchill has suffered seriously, but ten miles away it appears to be as primitive and uninterfered with as ever. Five hundred miles to the south, a car road today extends as far as The Pas. Churchill itself can now be reached by plane. But there is still the delightful weekly train and its leisured trek a thousand miles north from Winnipeg, across the great central prairies, through the vast forest belt of the North, out on to the arctic tundra.

I want to make very special acknowledgment to the following people who read through the manuscript of

this book with the most helpful and entertaining comments:

Dr. Arthur A. Allen, professor of Ornithology at
Cornell University, widely known for his wonderful
work with birds and photography and for various famous and fruitful scientific expeditions in tropical and
arctic America. Dr. Allen greatly helped and inspired
me with my first views of tundra birds, and is one of
my best-loved teachers.

Dr. and Mrs. Frederick M. Baumgartner, of Still-
water, Oklahoma. Mrs. Baumgartner, known especially
for authentic and inspiring articles on birds, was the
first American college girl to travel completely on her
own to far-off Churchill to study tundra birds, in particular the nesting habits of the tree sparrow. It was she
who first inspired me to visit the Far North and introduced me to the fascination of exploring an arctic tundra; and she generously gave me free access to her own
Hudson Bay notes, letters, and photographs. Dr. Baumgartner, professor of Wildlife Conservation and Ornithology at Oklahoma Agricultural and Mechanical
College, a member of the Cornell expedition of 1934 to
Hudson Bay, also kindly corroborated the descriptions
and details in this manuscript.

Mrs. Eva Beckett, who for sixteen years has lived at
Churchill from June through December, and is well

known for delightful and valuable writings on arctic natural history in Canadian magazines. To her, with her years of experience in various parts of the Arctic and Subarctic, has fallen the heaviest task of checking over this book for inaccuracies or inconsistencies.

Dr. George M. Sutton, curator of birds and associate professor of Zoology at the University of Michigan, a foremost artist and naturalist, to whom I am particularly indebted for the painting in this book which makes the tundra so beautiful and so real. Dr. Sutton's checking of the manuscript has been very valuable since he is an authority on arctic natural history.

The aid of various other people also has been most important in my gaining vivid impressions of the North. Lieutenant Colonel John Stanwell-Fletcher, with his years of experience in the Arctic, helped me especially to acquire the general atmosphere and background of the life of northern men. With Miss Hazel R. Ellis, professor of Biology at Keuka College, I had on my second Churchill visit delightful and profitable field trips. And various friends around Churchill itself have extended wonderful hospitality to me (especially Mr. and Mrs. Angus MacIver) and given me all kinds of assistance. If there is anything here which is contrary to the very real firsthand knowledge and years of actual experience all these people possess, I hope they will be lenient, and bear in mind that human factors of Churchill today may differ considerably from those of the period which forms the setting for this story.

June

One

ᘓᘓᘓᘓᘓᘓᘓᘓᘓᘓᘓᘓᘓᘓᘓᘓᘓᘓᘓᘓᘓᘓᘓ

AFTER IT LEFT the last bit of northern spruce forest and
crossed several miles of tundra late this afternoon of
the 23rd of June, our lengthy train of aged freight and
passenger cars pulled up, very leisurely, to the little
station of Churchill — the northernmost point of steel
in Canada. About sixty people were standing around.
This is Churchill's entire population, which gathers
regularly to meet the one train — its chief link with the
outside world — that travels a thousand miles north
from Winnipeg once a week in summer, every two or
three in winter, to reach this small subarctic outpost at
58° 56′ north latitude on the west coast of Hudson Bay.

There were Indians as well as white people, and off
by themselves four short, stocky figures with striking
dark round faces — my first Eskimos. And, thank heav-
en, there were Sue (her skin has turned completely
brown; with that brunette style of hers she looked exactly like another particularly jolly little Eskimo), and

[3]

Dr. Stevens, so tattered and tanned he simply wasn't recognizable. There were groups of men in shabby, nondescript attire whose faces gave a fleeting impression of being anything but nondescript. There was the usual effective Mountie, scarlet-coated for an important occasion, whom you learn to associate with every northern Canadian settlement, a girl and a baby with him, and a few women among the numbers of men. And beyond the station, a handful of small buildings, a few widely-scattered shacks, a low rise of land with the towering wires of a radio station, stretched a desolate immensity of sky and an endless field of ice.

There is nothing here *but* sky and ice and rocks, with a few shacks like tiny toys thrown in. It all looks rather like those pictures of Byrd's expedition in the Antarctic. The air is perfectly marvelous — so deeply strong and utterly clean and exhilarating.

After a confusion of greeting Dr. Stevens and Sue, both in the height of spirits and sunburns, and the two Canadian scientists who've been working with them, and of collecting bags and duffels, I learned that I was to be quartered in a tent on the slope above Sue's one-room shack because the shack is filled completely with Sue and bird specimens, while the tent overlooks Hudson Bay, and I "like space and views." Sue and one

Terence, a big man with a bush of white hair, a huge nose, and astonishingly blue eyes who seemed to have proprietary rights on me and the aforesaid tent, and a strange youth, all laden with my baggage, deposited me finally at the tent; and Terence and Sue pointed out landmarks.

There wasn't a sound except wild, occasional gusts of wind and howls from a sled dog, until one of the wierdest noises you ever heard, a series of sort of un-earthly cries, suddenly rent the air, adding immeasur-ably to the eeriness and loneliness of everything. "Just the ducks — old-squaws — coming into the town slough," they informed me, delighted at my nervous start.

Sue, rather offensively exuding self-reliance and health, said I'm to be called on later to watch the sun-set, and dashed away to gather up incoming mail.

The dear Lord knows when anyone goes to bed here. It's after nine and I'm ready for it this minute. After five long nights and days on trains, at the moment I didn't want to look at sunsets, or anything for that mat-ter. But I had to listen politely to Terence who, with the silent young man whom no one introduced, showed off this "nice large tent," about twelve by seven feet, with a rough plank floor and boards going part way up the sides, a tiny iron stove, pipe carefully projected through a square of tin to the outside, a bunk and straw mattress, and the wood door with a strong hook inside. Having had experience with tents, I'm appreciative of these luxuries, though dubious at the assurance that "a body could live in it in pairfect comfort in winter even." Despite the stout boards and floor to which it's anchored, heavy gusts shake it violently.

Terence explained that the tar-papered shack marked "Cafe," about ten yards away (how *is* one to get any privacy?), is his and the only one in Churchill; that he is renting tourist tents this summer (this appears to be the only one); that anything in the way of food, water, and protection is mine for the asking. All this and other bits of general information were delivered in a Canadian accent with flavors of brogue and a voice surprisingly soft for such a big person. At last he and the still completely speechless young man took themselves off, with a parting finale from Terence:

"Is this ye're first visit to the North, Miss Reeve? Well then, it won't be ye're last either. Everybody always comes back to Churchill — !"

I put on ski pants and other baggy old clothes to match Sue, and went outside again. Gosh, but it's cold here! Churchill, situated at the mouth of the Churchill River, is on a small narrow neck of land pointing north; about 400,000 square miles of sea, which is Hudson Bay, lie east; on the west the broad river empties out between two very low ridges, which apparently form the only rocky outcrop and practical harbor in hundreds of miles of flat shallow coastline. Besides the tiny houses and shacks, scattered sparsely over a mile or two, belonging to about seventeen families who live at Churchill, there are two or three small stores — one, white with red roof, the Hudson's Bay Company (note Hudson's Bay Company and Hudson Bay, not vice versa); small maroon buildings along the tracks; and an incongruously huge and unpleasantly conspicuous concrete grain elevator completed recently to house produce from the prairies which, now that the Hudson Bay railroad is finished, is to be shipped each summer via Hudson Bay to Europe. There's a little white church and, situated on a low rise slightly above the rest of Churchill, a radio station and small barracks, also neatly white and red-roofed, of the Royal Canadian Mounted Police. South beyond Terence's café is a gray Catholic mission building with a tower.

Beyond this tent the slope rises gradually to a gravel bank above the sea; this broadens out north and south into a narrow, low ridge of rocks. Another reach of land, dimmed blue by distance, lies beyond the big river which is two miles wide for some eight miles above its entrance into Hudson Bay. Until June 21, just two days ago, when the river ice went out all at once, as it invariably does around this time of year, "Like the whole river's gone out to sea," Terence said (bets as to the exact date are a feature of Churchill), Indians and white trappers have been driving dog teams over it.

I was gazing around feeling a bit strange and scared, wondering whether it's all sort of beautiful or only just frightfully grim and desolate, when the windy gusts unexpectedly started to drop. Then all the great gray cloud banks spread overhead began to flush, deeper and deeper and deeper. As far as the eye could see — and it can stretch very far in this treeless, hill-less place — not just the west but the whole of a crimson and salmon cloud-tossed sky, colors spreading every second, was reflected in a flaming radiance from the vast white expanse of Hudson Bay.

There couldn't be anything like it anywhere else in the world except perhaps on the desert, but there you don't have a thousand miles of ice throwing back the colors.

There was a soft freshness of salt sea mingled with the cold breath of ice, which seems to mean Hudson Bay. A bell from the Catholic mission tolled out, clear and sudden in the brilliant, silent world. And it was followed instantly by another sound that made your hair rise and your heart stand still. Every single sled dog in Churchill — over two hundred Terence says — started by the bell or perhaps by the spell of sunset, must have begun to sing. There were no barks, only sustained sound, a tremendous harmony of living voices, fierce and exquisite and weird, swelling wildly, ebbing and dying, and rising again. It was the most moving, awesome, thrilling music I've ever heard in all my life. It was made of all the things one dreams of: the heartless beauty of arctic ice, the terror of polar winds and whirling snows, the short and radiant brightness of arctic summer, the undying loveliness of Lapland nights.

If I never experience anything else in all the North, to hear just this has been worth the traveling of any thousands of miles.

The sunset would fade, I thought, and Sue would miss it all. But it *hasn't* faded. After a whole hour the brilliance, unbelievably, is there still. The great dog chorus died gradually; now there are just a few lone and tragic voices singing with melting sadness to each other. They sound not so much miserable or suffering, but rather as I feel, filled with longings and dreams and a comprehension of something so unbearably big, that it makes them sad. . . .

Same night, but much later! Interrupted here by the advent of Sue and the others, arrived finally to introduce me to a northern evening on Hudson Bay. Now I'm

[9]

back in the tent again, in the sleeping bag to keep warm. The wood bunk and straw pallet are hard as a rock. I'm simply dead, but can't sleep a wink. Won't be fit for a thing tomorrow. Perhaps if I get everything off my chest in a lengthy discourse now it will help.

I've sworn to my beloved brother Bill, off on archaeology business in Asia, to write up a "strictly accurate and detailed account — no omissions" of my first venture into arctic lands. But there were such fascinating things to do and people to talk to on the journey up that I haven't been able to achieve anything as yet except the merest of telegrams and post cards to the family.

The family, darling Mother excepted, seems to consider Bill's occupation so much more respectable than mine! Because he's a man? Or simply because archaeology has to do with human cultures rather than raw earth and "lowdown animal creatures?"

It's nice Bill and I've always been so much more congenial than most brothers and sisters seem to be. And that he does love birds and beasts and things. (Though not perhaps as intensely as I!) Anyway, after all the dissertations he's treated us to on his ancient ruins (I'm really grateful for the quite astonishing amount of information I've absorbed), *I* now propose to write up something on arctic natural history. I am

[10]

to keep detailed notes and reports of this summer's work for the university anyhow.

Almost midnight, and still there's no safe and familiar dark. A pale, radiant sort of brightness from the vivid northern twilight is filtering through the canvas. You can see clearly to read print or write. It was after eleven before we all came in at last. And the sunset was still there all across the north; brilliant salmons and golds deepened into red and darker rose; the ice roughened into shadowed pinnacles and queer shapes of pink and green, extending in the distance in brown and purple masses. There was surely never, anywhere, so much sky and color. If it had been warm enough to just keep still and watch, you could have been drowned in it, simply drugged into unconsciousness. But we all had to tramp about vigorously while we talked.

The two middle-aged Canadians, Mr. Clayton and Dr. Carey, are nice; the one huge and lively, bald and messy, the other small and quiet, neat and gray-haired. Dr. Stevens came to the tent to fetch me, rattled the door and called out, "Are you there?" Said I, "Oh yes, do come in" (forgetting that tents in this country possess securely fastened doors). Said he, "How shall I come? Down the stovepipe?" This is now my revered professor!

Everyone talked about living quarters. It appears

that in lieu of any other vacant place — there is no such thing as a hotel of course — the men, hospitably taken in by the minister, sleep on the upper floor of the little United Church of Canada. They all discussed locations of plants and birds they've been hunting, and prospects of better photography, since the weather which has been difficult, now looks good. We are all to start out at 7:30 A.M. tomorrow with the little dinkey engine which daily hauls a load of workmen some miles back past a water tower and lake situated on a stretch of tundra near timberline — an ideal area especially productive of wildlife.

All evening Sue has been pouring in my private ear fascinating (and disquieting) fragments of information on Churchill and its inhabitants. I'll be "quite safe," she says in the tent if tough characters appear — "there certainly are queer ones around" — because Terry will chase them off!

She wanted to get something at Hobson's, one of the small trading stores, so we took a walk down there. Picturesque-looking Indians seemed to be having a late evening tea party on a wooden platform outside the store. The store, scarcely as large as our parlor at home, was very clean and trim. It seemed to contain everything anyone in the North could possibly want from food and clothing, fox furs, caribou sleeping bags and medicines, to steel traps, books and guns. "Si" Hobson, the proprietor, is a lean, quiet, middle-aged man with a pleasant face, but it was Mrs. Taylor, his partner, who intrigued me especially — also solid and middle-aged with a rope of dark brown hair round her head, bright hazel eyes, and striking facial lines. An air of knowing life and accepting with equanimity what it has brought her and what she has chosen to do with it, is written all over her. All sorts of people, from well-to-do whites to forlorn-looking Indians, kept coming in while we were there and all were treated with equally pleasant efficiency. Children haunted the footsteps of Mrs. Taylor.

There was a door at the back opening into a small room containing an iron stove, pots and pans, a table, cupboards, bookcases, and a large inviting bed. "Sure, that's where 'Si' and Mrs. Taylor live," remarked Sue with a grin at me when we were outside again. "That's where they sleep in on stormy days like the rest of Churchill does; no one ever thinks of disturbing them when the door's fastened — "

"But — ?"

"Just forget New England and the Pilgrim Fathers, Rosy my love," said my uninhibited western friend. "People in the North who do the oddest things are so *nice!* There're a lot more of the perfectly conventional couples around here too, but no one seems to be thought of one bit more affectionately than the Hobsons!"

In addition to the regular citizens of Churchill, there are groups of men who come in seasonally to work on the railroad, harbor, and grain elevator, trappers who spend the summer, groups of Chipewyan and Cree Indians, occasional Eskimos. (The Indian population, roughly, extends as far north as the tree limit, beyond that the Eskimos begin.) Various other sorts of people — scientists, writers, missionaries — pass through or stay for short periods. The majority of the inhabitants are English-, Scotch-, and Irish-Canadians, but there is a quite fair proportion of Scandinavians — Norwegians, Swedes, Danes, and Icelanders.

On the other side of the railroad track along rocky and willow-grown flats that border the Churchill River, we could see scattered about a dozen or more canvas tents, each with its protruding stovepipe and numerous dogs tied outside. These belong to the white men who trap foxes and other fur-bearers inland or on the Barrens north of Churchill. They are, says Sue, the most fascinating of all! "They may be tough, but they are men if you please." Some are well educated, some completely illiterate. Most of them spend the summer around Churchill; and there are two especially — Danish or Swedish or something! They really have manners and have been to Oxford or some place. No one seems to know much about them, but they come to the café and hobnob with Terence.

Sue said, nastily, "Just exert a little of that charm of yours and find out about them. . . . I know you — you will soon anyway!"

I've been grinning at the thought of reactions to all this sort of thing from our beloved relatives. "This" is so exactly "the type of impossible situation Rosamund would rejoice in." So tragic that with her background Rosamund does such queer things in unheard-of places.

"Look where Rosamund's preferences and her reckless taste for adventure have almost led her." (Only I know how nearly!) And those odd foreign acquaintances — Bill's been responsible for a few himself — who've appeared now and then. . . . Charming Mother, embarrassing Father, but to whom he always extends the same gentle courtesy that he would to the President of Harvard, because he is a gentleman and a dear, and tolerant inside. There *is* something to be said for breeding.

And, of course, I've remembered Horace; and feel rather upset suddenly to remember how little I *have* remembered him. He saw me off on the train, having just bought a new and shining Ford coupé, eminently respectable and practical. This is what he always will buy, never a convertible. He would never really enjoy wind in his hair. With him all of life will be like this: wear well, be secure and careful and dependable. What sensible people strive for. Dear "old Horry" — he would be called by something that could never be made into a respectable nickname — he's such a swell person. But it will be a relief to forget him for awhile.

He'd have disapproved most thoroughly of my journey up. (He was very hurt anyway — one of his most irritating and touching characteristics — at the whole idea of this summer's trip and the work for the university.) From the minute I started across Canada and recovered from the sensation of being so completely on my own, I enjoyed it hugely.

The train trip from Winnipeg five hundred miles north to The Pas (though it was as nothing compared with the next from The Pas to Churchill) was really swell. Such a long shabby unconventional train of very old passenger cars, bursting with women and babies and children at each stop, which occurred at least every half hour; chugging slowly over flat prairies or unimpressive rolling wooded country.

Across the aisle in the one aged Pullman, there was a husky, chubby-faced young man with blond hair that stood straight up, a really awful tie, and a far from attractive suit of clothes. But he looked so rosy and possessed such a twinkling eye that I got to be great pals with him. Mr. Winston Jones, en route to Flin Flon, that new and fabulous mining center beyond The Pas, is a mining engineer. Flin Flon, its name supposedly derived from the character in a book which its original discoverer had been reading, sounds most gay and enchanting but is not, I was given to understand, at all like its name. What a name! So unlike sober, historic Boston, Concord, Salem, Plymouth. Probably, I imagine (without as yet knowing much about it), rather like life of the North — whimsical, not necessarily respectable, names counting very little.

There was a long day's wait at The Pas. Another whimsical appellation made of two languages. And no one could tell me why it has not remained Le Pas or been completely changed to its English equivalent. A small sprawled-out town, situated on the banks of the north Saskatchewan River, it was prominent in early history and is very important now as a distribution center for supplies and to people going farther north. Broad, muddy roads and large numbers of huge, fierce-looking, heavily-furred dogs (used on sleds in winter, Mr. Jones informed me) seemed to be its chief features. There were small stores, a number of them fur traders', little frame houses, an old Anglican church, a Catholic hospital, police and customs offices, a drab hotel or two.

Across the bridge that spanned the broad Saskatchewan, were small huts and tents, part of a Cree Indian settlement, and flat wild land stretching endlessly away in monotonous forests of small spruce and poplar. Roads led only a short way out of town and nothing but the railroad connects it with other distant settlements.

At this point, feeling rather too much on my own, I gratefully accepted the escort of Mr. Jones. In this world, it's a person, not clothes or background, one associates with. My own very plain suit seemed suddenly rather too well cut, its heather mixture unnecessarily nice with a black hair-gray eyes sort of combination. I felt altogether too small and innocent-looking for this rough and tough jumping-off place.

Before the Churchill train left to proceed yet farther north, Mr. Jones and I shared a meal at a restaurant. And when he stepped out to find a paper, the huge and blowsy proprietress wandered over and fell into lazy conversation.

"Going Nort' widt your husband?" she inquired.

"Oh, he's not my husband," I hastened to reply, much too quickly, for the fat lady winked hugely, leered, and promptly ambled off. (Imagine the disgust of Horace! The amusement of Mother!)

When at last I boarded the train late in the afternoon, cheered by a farewell from Jones who remained refreshingly merry and matter-of-fact to the last, I found it, except for the substitution of numerous freight for passenger cars, substantially the same train as the one on which we traveled from Winnipeg. There was, however, a different and even older Pullman full of strange men, all going to Churchill. There was a French-Canadian priest who said he couldn't see why anyone would take this God-forsaken place from the Indians; two young Canadians going to take on jobs in the new Churchill grain elevator; an overalled, jolly-faced man, something important to do with the railroad, whom everyone treated with affection and respect; a red-haired Scotsman called Sandy of course; an H.B.C. (Hudson's Bay Company) man, whose rugged countenance was vastly interesting; a sad and lonely-looking young wireless operator. One chap, tall and young, excessively spare and witty, was in particular friendly and intriguing. This was Duncan Scott, who has a job of importance with the Harbor Board, or something, at Churchill to which he is returning after a holiday outside.

I was the only female. In fact there appeared to be no other women on the entire Churchill run. But the atmosphere of the car was so completely informal, its occupants so unique and respectful, I ceased to feel shy and instead was delightfully thrilled. At one end of the car was a kitchenette, and two sections with card tables were reserved for eating. The tall, old, and handsome Negro porter (so incongruous in these arctic wastes), presided impressively over the business of his car, serving neat, hot little meals to each passenger in turn, collecting tickets with somber formality, making up berths with rapid efficiency; and woe to anyone whose behavior did not meet with approval from his eagle eye.

It *was* rather exhausting to be such a center of attention. They were all so crazy to talk. But who could blame them when any outsider, especially a young female in a land where females obviously are as scarce as hen's teeth, must be a perfect Godsend.

Duncan Scott sat by me frequently and produced letters from a friend at Churchill which, to my edification and that of the entire Pullman population which leaned across the aisle and hung over backs of seats, he read out loud. The letters, in addition to being informative about Churchill, contained frequent references to the scientists who have come to work here this summer and, for some reason, especially interested speculations on the personality and future welfare of Miss Susan Henderson's friend, Miss Rosamund Reeve. And at each of these Mr. Scott with a grin like a nudge in the ribs would pause, while the other gentlemen beamed on Miss Reeve's flushed countenance.

And there was a gaunt trapper, "Slim Jim," whom I sat opposite to as luck would have it for two meals, who was really unbelievable. He too had been outside but was now, "Thank God," returning to a country where he could get deer meat fit to eat, and a climate where it was cool enough to live. Under the jacket and open plaid shirt, he was wearing (honestly!) two sets of long-sleeved Jaeger underwear and he was obliged to stop eating frequently to sop his streaming countenance with the snowy napkin which did chief duty as a towel. While I'm at Churchill he'll take me in his boat on the river any time. . . . He drank modestly from a flattish bottle of gigantic proportions (I hadn't known whisky bottles ever came that size), which he wore inside his coat and was respectfully surprised when I politely re-fused to join him. And each time, bless his heart, until I protested violently, he started to pay for my meals. Said "Shucks," he had "a plenty" left from trapping last year! The porter, wise doubtless from experience, ap-peared to be completely indulgent of any of these kinds of oddities.

There was something about all those men, entirely regardless of outward appearance and occupation, with their complete dignity and very true, if unconventional, courtesy, their apparent calm acceptance of life as they find it, that compared more than well with the impeccably-turned out, perpetually grousing businessmen, the cultured, finicky professors of our accustomed world.

And when I was not being vastly intrigued by my fellow travelers, I was somehow surprised and deeply thrilled by what we saw from the car windows as the train went ever northward slowly and smoothly across five hundred solid miles of flat, utterly wild and untouched land.

The first evening and night after The Pas, we passed endless forests of spruce and poplar, and lakes so winding and wild, that it made the mouth of one from a land where lakes are a rarity, fairly water. The night was the most restful I ever spent on a train. The car was completely quiet and dark, though the light northern evening outside seemed to go on forever and change imperceptibly into early morning. Except for infrequent stops where sled dogs were howling eerily, there was no break in the gentle motion and the slow clack of wheels. No curves, no other trains to pass, no noise-filled stations, no towns, no lights. Sometime in the middle of the night it got bitterly cold and I had to shut the open window which had felt so delicious at The Pas, and pile all my clothes and coat on top of the berth blankets.

The second day we passed through the False Barrens, so-called. Here for miles and miles forest growth was absent completely, or so sparse that trees were gray spindly sticks bearing nothing except clusters of dead foliage at their tops. They looked like long-handled mops upside down. Sometimes the slender branches only grew from one side, streaming like banners to lee-ward, as though all the trees had been sliced clean on the other side. There were slow-winding streams and ditches of gold-brown water, occasional rivers (the Nel-son being the largest and most famed), more lakes or little swampy ponds. Except for water reflecting blue sky, it was all a vast monotonous gray and brown.

"Why the hell don't we go faster?" one of the new grain elevator youths inquired that second day. "Be-cause the wheels'd skid on ice!" called someone.

The straight gravel road bed has been laid carefully for the single train track across those hundreds of miles of wet, treacherous muskeg. As you get farther up to-ward Churchill there is solid ice a few feet below surface all the year round. Telegraph poles, which follow the railroad all the way, are seldom placed singly and up-right but arranged in threes like a sloping tripod. This is the only way that they can be kept secure on such unstable ground, Duncan Scott informed me.

Shed caribou horns scattered on mossy mounds indicated the great caribou migrations; and ptarmigan still in partially white winter plumage, crouched on banks everywhere, or took short, funny, little flights. Occasional stops were made to deliver mail or a lonely passenger at some trackman's shack. Some of these were stations bearing impressive names on the timetable; some were just Mile 261 or Mile 300 (from The Pas). Our own Pullman group, mingling with Indians and breeds, rough men from the other cars, and the train crew, all alike descended to stroll about while the train, without any apparent reason, lingered for a half hour or more. "Crew's got to rest," Duncan Scott reminded me, "and the guys who live here've got to have a chance to talk to someone and get news and things — "

At every stop, the quality of the chill air scented with odors of spicy bogs and evergreens, the wildness and stillness of it all, somehow stirred me as no atmosphere has ever quite done before. Loving mountains and forests so, I'd thought these regions would be chiefly desolate and wasn't prepared for their strangely gripping quality. This country, which even now in late June, spring has scarcely touched, is cold and unwelcoming. Yet its complete repose and serenity, its strength and cleanness, somehow seem more stirring than the most exotic beauty.

After the stretches of Barrens came forest again,

small densely packed black spruce. Even though Churchill itself marks the beginning of subarctic tundras and the end of timberline, inland from the coast of Hudson Bay, they told me, lonely isolated fingers of forest still reach northward sixty miles or more.

By afternoon of the second day when we had almost completed those long five hundred and ten miles from The Pas to Churchill, it grew even colder (everyone — except Slim Jim — had been dressed all day in extra sweaters and overcoats). Suddenly the Pullman curtains, still shrouding the form of the wireless operator, who in a completely quiet and inoffensive way apparently had imbibed so much the night before that he was unable to rise, parted unexpectedly. A very red nose appeared in the slit and a hoarse voice demanded:

"Have we got to Gillam yet? 'Ve got to see someone — "

Gillam, numbering about a hundred inhabitants, the chief settlement between The Pas and Churchill, having been reached, stopped at for hours, and left far behind early in the morning, this caused an outbreak of mirth that lasted our entire car all the way to Churchill.

One A.M. Still light inside the tent. One more look outside. . . . There's not a sound, not a movement. Churchill and its people, its dogs, its train, are still as death, insignificant nothings in a vastness of ice field and tundra.

But the sunset has changed into a motionless rich, deep orange over all the north, and dawn is beginning to brighten the northeast. The sky, now perfectly clear, is a great, deep, sapphire ceiling. The white ice has grown slatey. Here is the miracle of a world, in which even for a brief season, there is no night. It seems a sort of presage for days to come; a consolation that such a thing is real. I'm desperately sleepy — at last. The wood bunk really feels good, the down bag wonderful —

Two

~~~~~~

THE 25TH OF JUNE. What a day on the tundra yesterday! I emerged from the depths of exhausted sleep after my first night at Churchill surrounded, quite literally, by the most heavenly bird songs. In a tent you're right out in it all as you never can be inside solid walls. It was simply enchanting. There were myriads of silvery tinkles from horned larks, our relative of the European skylark, but what on earth made the regular showers of rippling notes just overhead?

It was long after 7 A.M.; almost time to start on the dinkey, in fact. Scarcely time to dress and get a bite of breakfast at Terence's. I hustled on the old, gray winter skisuit (about right for summer on Hudson Bay), rubber boots, tam and gloves, grabbed the knapsack, which, thanks to a few sad past experiences, I now keep always ready packed, Leica and glasses, and rushed outside.

Thirty feet above the tent, a small bird on out-

stretched wings and tail hung suspended in the glorious
sky of a clear subarctic summer's morning; then floated
gently down on wave upon wave of bubbling melody
to light on the ridgepole. A plump and sparrowlike bird,
with the richest of colors — crown, face and throat dense
black, creamy white above the eyes; breast white, with
black side streaks, and the rest patterned in ocher, red-
browns and blacks. It was easily recognizable from the
bird books as a Lapland longspur, that arctic member
of the finch and sparrow groups, prominent alike in
Lapland, Siberia, and our own arctic America, whose
very long hind toenail is like a spur stretched out behind.

Longspurs were everywhere. A pair by the tent,
others nearby, climbing high into the sky and floating
down, males vying with each other in the ardor of their
spirits. The crystal blue morning was all alive with their
ecstatic, bubbling songs and the larks' exquisite, harp-
sichord tinklings.

And you *never* felt such divine air. Hot sun and salt
sea and cold ice all mixed intoxicatingly together. Here,
exactly at sea level, there is that same superb exhilara-
tion of high mountains, but there is none of the breath-
lessness of the great heights.

There was no sign of a dinkey or anyone down by
Sue's shack, but even if I missed them all I had to eat.
Hadn't had a thing since a light supper the afternoon

of the day before. In the café I was greeted by a good-natured, sleepy Terence, white hair on end, trousers imperfectly buttoned over pajamas (must have just stepped out of bed, but he was completely unperturbed, and the stove in the tiny kitchen partitioned off from the main room was hot). The main room, about eighteen by ten feet, was filled with two benches, a long oilcloth covered table on which reposed used dishes, shaving things, a basin of dirty water; and spread on the bare floor were two aged sleeping bags, one of which still contained a mummylike form, doubtless the silent young man. Terence plied me with tea so black that I supposed it was coffee until I tasted it, and hefty slices of homemade bread, damp, delicious, and frightfully indigestible.

When I reached Sue's fifteen minutes later they were all there, fortunately, still waiting for the dinkey, which, after all, didn't appear till long past eight.

I observed several more prominent Churchill institutions I'd missed the night before. One, not far from Sue's shack, is a small building about thirty feet long marked, in huge gold letters, along its black-tar papered side: BANK OF MONTREAL. And farther along toward the town slough is a ramshackle little house even more important and extensively patronized — the Chinese laundry.

"Do you object to my smoking?" said a voice in my ear.

Startled, I turned from absorbed contemplation of the morning as we sat swinging our feet from the little open car which the dinkey, a sort of toy engine about as high as a tall man, pulled lightly and jerkily along the narrow gauge track across the tundra. The exceedingly nice voice came from one of the blue-overalled, oil-begrimed workmen crowded onto the car. But this one was sitting next to me with a merry eye fixed on mine. Intrigued, I fell into enthusiastic conversation, discovering that he was a young Scot recently "come over." He had a most attractive, well-educated personality under the grime and the overalls and he talked exceedingly well on the fascination of the Northland. He said he has a place on the Isle of Skye and, though he thinks it more beautiful over there than here, there is something about the lands of the tundra one has to keep coming back to. What he was doing here working on a railroad I wished I could find out. But the dinkey had reached the water tower and was stopping to let us off.

Mr. Clayton and Dr. Carey, laden with cameras and plant presses, vanished at once in opposite directions in a sternly purposeful manner, while Sue and Dr. Stevens undertook to show me around. When you are out in it all, a part of it, on your own two feet, the vastness of

sky and distance, the great unsoiled cleanness and freshness become even more striking than before. Hundreds
of little lakes, and a thousand pools, lay scattered everywhere as we tramped across slippery, cushion-soft
mosses of tundra or waded knee-deep in ice-cold, grassy
ponds of muskeg. (I at once discovered the reason for
Sue's emphatic orders to obtain "lightweight, comfortable *hip* boots at all costs.")

The difference, about which I've been somewhat con-
fused, between tundra and muskeg was apparent. The
former is composed of slightly elevated, drier hummocks
of lichens, chiefly the Cladonia or reindeer moss, often
mixed with prostrate arctic willows, dwarf birches, or
heathy plants like Labrador tea and Andromeda, Vacciniums, foot-high rhododendrons, and the occasional
tiny liverwort, *Marchantia polymorpha.* Tundra
mounds, Dr. Stevens says, are an example of climax
vegetation, which may eventually become yet drier and
more built up with woody plants. Muskeg, on the other
hand, is a definitely swampy part of tundra or northern
forest. Its soft, treacherous mucky places and little pools
are surrounded with Eriophorums, the cotton grass,
sedges, and Equisetums.

The great, flat tundra world was just teeming with
bewildering numbers of birds. Species familiar and
species entirely new to me, rare and mentioned with

bated breath by ornithologists at home, were pointed out every second by the others who, having already been some weeks in this country, have gotten in the essential spade work of identifying and nest-finding.

Hovering jaegers, gulls, terns, and snipe screamed and circled high in the sky; larks and longspurs (here were Smith's as well as Lapland) were tumbling in the air singing directly overhead; redpolls, tree and white-crowned sparrows, black-poll warblers, willow ptarmigans, burst from willow thickets around the lakes. Semipalmated plovers ran agitatedly over mosses and gravelly outcrops. The earth was filled with the sweet and plaintive cries of least and semipalmated sandpipers, wheeling through the air in compact little flocks, silver when white of their wings caught sunshine, gray and black when dark parts flashed uppermost. Arctic loons, tiny phalaropes, pintail ducks, and old-squaws called wildly across the ponds.

Old-squaws are the clowns of the tundra. They sound both wild and comical, completely appropriate somehow to a tundra land. As they rush past you, their cry is a ludicrous "owl-owl-omelette, owl-owl-omelette," rather like a travesty on an automobile horn, emphasis on the "om." And their plump brown bodies with white patchings in disorderly array (they've not yet entirely acquired their full summer plumage), the two elongated tail feathers of the male, the almost bald appearance of the white splotched heads, the funny, excited way they take off from water or flounder sideways as they land, their odd courting habit of snapping the head back and jerking the body forward, all remind one exactly of a clown.

There were nests everywhere. Every few yards in fact. It was all so open and the birds so tame you almost stepped on them. Regular nest hunting de luxe. All the birds, hundreds and thousands of them, were singing and screaming, scolding and courting and nesting with the utmost intensity, as if they must make the most of every single minute of each unspeakably wonderful day of the short summer.

"Just wait," Dr. Stevens, who has spent previous summers in the North, said ominously. "A few more days of this and mosquitoes'll begin and you won't think anything's wonderful!"

Instead of the Misses Henderson and Reeve by which titles for three solid years he has so respectfully addressed two of his prize graduate students, we've become a sudden and flippant Black-eyed Susan and Arctic Rose. I keep wondering if this naughty, mud-spattered, wiry individual, sandy red hair on end, black eyes snapping, can honestly be that much revered head of the Zoo Department, so invariably well-groomed, so reserved, distinguished, and admired.

We covered a square mile or more and viewed some dozens of nests, their location carefully marked with upright sticks or bits of paper. Some were mere depressions, hollowed out in mosses or grasses, containing sets of eggs or young just hatched. I tried to sort out for future reference distinguishing characteristics of the most common birds. The little semipalmated plovers with one black band across the white breast, black and white heads and bright orange-yellow legs, running along right beside us and scolding unceasingly, were most conspicuous. Their four pretty little, tan, black-specked eggs were placed most casually on a completely open patch of gravel. The semipalmated and least sandpipers on the other hand, are very difficult; both so small and streaked and inconspicuous, the former with black legs, the latter with theirs greenish-yellow. The nest of the least sandpiper, a grass-lined hollow in wet muskeg, was hard to see and the shy little parent bird put on a gallantly brave performance, dragging pretended broken wings and calling agonizingly to distract attention from the eggs. The size of the eggs was astonishing. Could these four, sharply-pointed, huge things, about one and a quarter inches long, laid point to point, really belong to such a tiny pitiful creature?

There was a Smith's longspur; its nest much more carefully fashioned and lined with soft feathers in the side of a dry moss-decked hummock. The bird's coloring is charming; its throat and breast a lovely buff and yellow where the Lapland longspur is so black and white; but its song is shorter, far less musical and bubbling than that gay creature's. Here in a low clump of willow and alder and dwarf birch, were nests of the white-crowned sparrow and a black-poll warbler, figures familiar only in migration periods at home. And in a clump of small spruce, a rare find — a well-constructed, tiny, feather-lined nest of the hoary redpoll. I must spend long hours over this exquisite small bird.

Tree sparrows with their warm red-brown caps, almost our most common New England winter visitor, were nesting and singing everywhere — so very sweetly it made a lump come in your throat. It was the little snatch of song we hear at home on a warm late winter's day, always one of our first harbingers of spring, here intensified and multiplied a hundredfold.

Across that lake was an island covered with the eggs of arctic terns laid almost anywhere in ones or twos or occasionally threes, and the nest of an old-squaw. The blue sky was flecked white with the hundreds of indescribably graceful, indescribably noisy terns, and the waters echoed with the weirdly lovely and ghostly voices of a pair of arctic loons whose nest thus far has been sought in vain.

And so it went. No wonder Churchill, the only Canadian subarctic outpost recently become accessible by rail, is already beginning to be a Mecca for ornithologists. Five hundred miles below the Arctic Circle, it lies at the northern line of timber species and the southern line of arctic ones. A mere few years ago if a naturalist wanted to study arctic birds on their Hudson Bay nesting grounds, he had to travel by boat one summer, way up north of Labrador and over into Hudson Bay, and stay the entire next winter in the lands of the Eskimo in order to be on hand for the following spring. It's only within these last few years that the nests of many of these birds, except on very rare occasions, have been seen and described at all.

I am to spend the next few days becoming acclimated and familiar with it all and then I, too, shall begin that fascinating and arduous work of bird photography, with special notes on habits and behavior, followed later when the flowers bloom, by plant collecting.

We circled back again toward the blue winding waters of Lake Rosabelle. Only two of the lakes are distinguished by a name. Isabelle, a mile or so long, lies farther east toward Hudson Bay. On a drier, more extensive stretch of tundra was a tiny bird blind, a khaki

canvas rectangle some four feet high by six wide, put
up by Dr. Stevens and Sue just six feet from the home
of a golden plover. Here they were to spend hours on
pictures of the parent plovers and two young, just
hatched.

Since the blind has been there some days, the plovers
now regard it as a harmless and inevitable blot on their
landscape. And as soon as either Dr. Stevens or Sue
walk off leaving the other inside the blind out of sight,
the plovers, since they can't count and supposing everyone has gone, in the manner of most birds reacting to a
blind, conveniently and shortly return to their nest
where they may be viewed in a close-up, most fascinat-
ingly intimate fashion. And would also, they hoped, call
back the two young which already wandered about on
their own, since there were two unhatched eggs still
to be incubated.

A golden plover in the flesh was the thrill of a lifetime
to me. The female, running anxiously about some forty
feet away (it was probably the male farther off — the
two sexes are so alike you can't determine them at
sight) was infinitely more gorgeous in actuality than in
the pictures. Its size, about ten and a half inches in
length, and its shape are like the common killdeer, but
the plover is so striking that it seems heavier and larger.
Its upper parts are all finely patterned in black and

white and a greenish-yellow — this last predominating so that, at a distance, the back appears to be gold. All the underparts, cheeks, and throat, down breast and belly, are the densest of black velvet. A broad band of pure white stretches over the forehead, above the eyes, and down sides of the breast. When the bird turns and runs with its quick flurried steps directly towards you, it reminds you exactly of a little old lady dressed in black, surmounted by her white wool kerchief, two ends falling gracefully upon black-clad shoulders.

Both plovers came near while I was there. They circled the mosses in a series of little runs, disappearing and reappearing behind low hummocks, uttering the most strangely sweet and melodiously metallic alarm notes, spaced distinctly one upon the other.

The two precocious babies, hatched the day before, of which we caught glimpses through the glasses as they ran about or hid under grasses and tussocks, were small fluffy balls of black and white and golden dots. Here was a perfect example of precocial young (characteristic of most shore and water birds), born of those parents who make little or no nests upon the ground and give their offspring scant protection. The babies are able to get about and feed themselves almost as soon as they emerge from the eggs, and require only occasional parental brooding for warmth.

The remaining two, lovely, grayish-tan plover eggs, about one and a half inches long, heavily splotched with black and dark brown, lay in a small depression of lavender and gray and yellow reindeer moss, and were the most exquisite illustration of protective coloration. They blended so exactly with surrounding grays and blacks, mauves and browns and yellow-greens of lichens and heath plants not yet in bloom; you could scarcely see them even a few feet off unless your eyes were glued on them. And if for a second you looked away at something else, you couldn't find them again.

Such is the American golden plover, one of the world's greatest of travelers (bird or human!), whose marvelous yearly journeyings to and from the nesting grounds make naturalists wax lyrical, and must inspire any perceptive human with reverence at the ways of animal life. For the travels of this plover have now been plotted accurately enough to satisfy even the most exacting scientist.

In midwinter starting north from southern Argentina, where it has spent a resting period of about a month after the many arduous months of autumnal migration, the golden plover negotiates the great Andes of Peru, and goes up the Pacific Ocean to the highlands of Honduras. Then on again over the Gulf of Mexico; and in March, still wearing its winter vest of gray instead of black, it begins a slow pilgrimage up the Mississippi Valley and north through Canada. Until in early June, having acquired again its brilliant black and gold, the plover reaches the land of the tundra and the midnight sun.

A scant two months for nesting and getting offspring into the world; and then in August they must all, including those precocial babies grown enough in just six or eight weeks to be able also to travel vast distances, be off before the arctic winter comes again.

This time there's a great southward march over entirely different territory. Across James Bay and Labrador to Newfoundland and Nova Scotia where the plover families linger to feed on crowberries and other luscious abundant northern fruits, until they've gained sufficient fat and energy to take them on again two thousand four hundred miles, over the Atlantic, Bermuda, and Venezuela to the Orinoco; another rest and still two thousand miles to go across vast jungles to south Brazil and Argentina.

For who knows how many thousands of years the American golden plover (the Pacific golden plover goes yearly from New Zealand and islands of the Antipodes to Alaska and back again) has traveled thus, without calendar, chart or compass, arriving and departing so unfailingly every single year in certain weeks or even on certain days that its observers in the Argentine, Peru, Honduras, the Mississippi, Hudson Bay, Labrador, Bermuda, Venezuela, the Orinoco, and Brazil can set their seasons by its presence, almost date their calendars.

I can't see that any of Bill's ancient human archaeological accomplishments are half as wonderful and thrilling as this.

Having promised to meet them all at five for the returning dinkey, I left the fascinating vicinity of the golden plover. Tucked in my pocket was a neat packet of Sue's patent "Tundra Lunch" of two rock-hard pilot biscuits, raisins and peanut butter in between, which knowing the confusion of a first morning, Sue put up for me in addition to her own.

Such is Sue. About the nicest kind of friend. Never dogging one's footsteps, but there when wanted. Somehow managing to do what other people need without perceptible exertion or diminution of her own activities. Her unflagging energy, though, is far beyond my lazy self who does so like to loll and dream — and am very sadly aware that Sue accomplishes infinitely more than I do.

After I'd walked some distance, in my excitement at chasing new birds following a wildly erratic course, I was startled by a series of loud, wild "tit-tit-tit-tit-tit" notes from a big brown bird which leapt into the air a few feet in front. A Hudsonian curlew of course. There was that distinctive silhouette against the sky; the small head with the great, three-inch, decurved bill, long legs, and a streaked brown body the size of a crow. Another extensive traveler who winters in South America and nests only in the Arctic. And over there was a second curlew rising up to join it. I was back in the vicinity of the curlew nest we'd all looked at earlier. There were the three blue little pools and the nest was near one shaped like a W. I stared and stared. Must have been mistaken. Certainly no nest or eggs here. And then precisely as though a wand had been waved, four eggs materialized in the exact spot at which I'd been gazing. About the size of hen's eggs, a little larger than the plovers', dull olive-green instead of tan, sprinkled less prominently with blotches of brown. Less spectacular than the plovers'. But what a ravishing setting! Little pools reflecting sky were the brightest of sapphires. Beside the eggs, a bit of pink, a dwarf rhododendron just flowering, made an exquisite color spot in the olive-green and yellow-brown pattern. Gray-tans and blacks of plovers' eggs with grays and mauves of reindeer moss, olives and browns of the curlews' with the greens and browns which here predominated.

If I retired behind that stunted spruce a hundred feet away to watch with glasses perhaps the curlews would stop their deafening noise and return to the nest. Sure enough, fifteen minutes later, they grew quiet, lit on the ground and began in wide circles of alternate runs and pauses to get nearer and nearer. Then one, the male perhaps, went off some distance while the other stood still midway between the nest and my tree, and began a fascinating drama of behavior.

It shooks its feathers elaborately, moistened the ridiculously long, unwieldy bill and passed it over wings and down the back, casting hurried nervous glances in my direction, looking away again quickly, rather touchingly trying to ignore my existence. The bird picked up leaves, small twigs, and moss and tossed them over its back in such an offhand, carefully careless manner I almost laughed out loud. "Be nonchalant and smoke a cigarette" idea.

All this went on for half an hour and in between the leaf-and-twig throwing exercises the curlew, in series of swift little runs, had been getting gradually closer and closer to the nest. Until, having reached it, with a great fluttering of wings and fluffing of breast down so the warm brood spots of bare skin could come in contact with the eggs, the bird settled as softly as a feather upon them, and became just an indistinguishable brown-streaked part of the tundra.

After a time, with infinite slowness and caution, I

rose, but the curlew which had been facing my spruce shot instantly into the air, as alarmed and upset and vociferous as before; and was joined at once by its mate who had not, as I'd supposed, left the vicinity at all.

Distressed at having caused such serious disturbance in the curlew family, I hurried off, to sit down later in the shade of another tiny clump of stunted spruce and low juniper on a less soakingly wet patch of mosses beside a small lake. My excellent raincoat which I spread out to lie on, I've already discovered to be a necessary part of tundra equipment even if it never rains. Grateful for shelter from a blazing sun I realized just how hot it had grown and looked avidly at the blue-green waters. There were no human signs, but my lake was just too exposed for a bath. There were dozens of little lakes all close at hand, or perhaps they were all part of this same one, winding enticingly about through tundra hummocks; all very shallow and crystal clear with gravel or gold-brown mucky bottoms; the gravel-bottomed ones emerald and aquamarine, the mucky-bottomed ones, where sunlight fell into them, a delicious and astonishing wine-dark red. They all freeze solid in winter and seem to be nearly empty of the usual aquatic plant and animal life of shallow lakes in temperate climes.

Just beyond Lake Isabelle, the low Rock Ridge —

50 to 75 feet in height — of ancient Pre-Cambrian granite stretches for several miles along Hudson Bay. A mile or so south of this particular flat, treeless, bird-filled stretch of muskeg and tundra and curving lakes, begin faint lines of small trees — white and black spruce and occasional light green larches — and a low rise of land leads up to an old abandoned gravel pit; this slight ridge in turn extends out to join the one by the bay.

For an hour I lay prone munching at the hardtack which, though it certainly takes a mighty effort to masticate, is quite satisfying. This was a place where it was wonderful to be alone. The thousand bird songs and calls were like a symphony. There was a low hum of insects, tiny bees and flies feeding on willow heads just beginning to open, little waves slapping the lake shore. The sun was hot and soothing; high overhead cold breezes from Hudson Bay, unchecked by hills or tall trees made a deep, very steady swishing background. Colorful, exquisitely-shaped little leaves, lichens, and mosses were spread everywhere. Scents of willows and heathy plants were delicious and exhilarating. Spicy and utterly clean and tonic. Nothing of the South here — exotic, overly sweet, or cloying — but something deeply health- and strength-giving, just like the North herself. There was the strangest combination of intimacy and safety with the lovely little things of the warm tundra floor, set over against the awesome bigness of sky and universe which nothing — no hill, no mountain or tree — obscures or sets in perspective.

Here you have a world composed of, and controlled by, living, animate, spiritual things and great creative forces — animals and plants, seas and ice, winds and storms, weather and seasons. Except for the train, the grain elevator, a few trucks that bump occasionally along the quarter mile of gravel which passes for a road in Churchill, life here has little to do with a soulless, mindless, machine-controlled existence.

I wondered why so many of these birds return generation after generation, braving the awful terrors of storm and sea and vast distance, to summer in this particular tundra world? The arctic terns every year travel miraculously even farther than the golden plovers, for they fly clean across the Atlantic, down the coasts of Europe and Africa all the way to the Antarctic, and back again up the coasts of the Americas; twice during twelve months negotiating great oceans; a single bird, during its one lifetime, perhaps, covering an incredible hundred thousand or two hundred thousand miles. *

---

* In June of 1944, Dr. Arthur A. Allen found on an island in Rosabelle Lake a dead arctic tern with a numbered leg band. When this band was checked by the banding branch of the Biological Survey, Washington, D. C., it was found that the tern had been banded as a nestling at Churchill by Albert L. Wilk July 10, 1937. This par-

It seemed to me that this involves something more than sexual or homing instincts, habits evolved from ancient climatic, glacial, or seasonal changes: all the fascinating theories and opinions put forth by scientists to explain the riddle of bird migraton. Perhaps some, or all, of these partly account for it. Here there is also an unlimited supply of water and food on every hand — tremendous insect life, any amount of crowberries, cranberries, blueberries, fish and mice and lemmings, various invertebrates. But important as all these are, I believe there is still something else less tangible — a sort of deep feeling for this kind of world; just as human beings experience profound joy from the wonderful air, the unending daylight, the lovely smells, the springy feel of lichens and mosses, hot sunshine and icy winds, the unlimited, unimpeded space of earth and sky. Again and again, like the birds, apparently, human beings return to it from the uttermost parts of the earth.

Look what happens in New England when you walk in a forest on a dark summer's day. There's a sparkle of sunlight and the utterly silent and seemingly lifeless woodland bursts into song and calls of a hundred birds. Pure pleasure inspires them, not a need for the physical

---

ticular tern, therefore, must have made seven round trips to the Antarctic via Europe and Africa, each trip involving some 22,000 miles, making a total of 154,000 miles. Arthur A. Allen, "Birds of Timberline and Tundra," *National Geographic* (Sept. 1946).

comforts of life which they have in abundance at this season anyway.

With these reflections, I drifted soundly into sleep and woke again only because it was icy cold. Heavens! This was not the world I'd gone to sleep in. Sunshine and temperatures of 70° or so, singing birds, and spicy smells were gone. A bitter wind and dark clouds of stinging mist, temperatures of 38°, were sweeping in from ice-filled Hudson Bay. (Such contrasts within a few hours often are recorded at Churchill.) This tundra world was desolate and colorless, wild and dangerous. I spent the remaining hour before returning to the water tower walking vigorously just to keep warm.

As, blue and shivering, we were all about to climb upon the dinkey car, Dr. Stevens, face crimson and shining with cold and mist, panting beneath the load of enormous hip boots, cameras, glasses, and tripod, came running, hurled himself on the car beside Sue and me, and cried:

"Kiss me quick! I've found a new bird's nest. . . ."

Really, if this is the effect of only a few short weeks on the tundra —

Three

~~~~~~

J UNE 30TH. Last evening, Eric Grey and Ronald McIntyre appeared. These are the trappers who so impressed Sue; as soon as I met them I realized I'd singled them out that first day at the station as two people who were especially noticeable. It's not their fine build and height, taller than average, but a poise of manner and an independence of bearing, that distinguishes them even here in this land of self-sufficient men whose strong bodies and weatherbeaten countenances make it hard to tell an age which may be almost anywhere between thirty and sixty. Mr. McIntyre, with his fair, clean-cut face is definitely attractive and pleasant to talk to. I'm less sure about Mr. Grey, whose cold, hard looks from penetrating, deep-set eyes give one a sort of shock, whose rugged features and shaggy, red-brown hair are not exactly handsome. But he *is* interesting!

After some very cold and stormy days, temperatures at 36° and 40° when everything was as gray and grim and desolate as the bleakest regions on earth, it became, suddenly and typically, an exquisitely beautiful evening; as warm and gentle and colorful as if this land were always summer. The mission bell had rung and the husky dogs had sung their thrilling mighty song — so beautiful and heart-rending, less wild and fierce than usual; softer and gentler somehow, in keeping with the evening.

Now, at the end of June, ice on the bay has really broken up at last and great white floes, according to wind direction, are moving in against the coast, or receding far seaward, leaving large areas of water. Last night the open water was far more extensive than before; instead of black, inky-blue or black-green, it was a soft turquoise, almost tropical blue, like pale shimmering satin, under the light blue northern sky. And white whales which we've seen heretofore only in the distance, were coming in close to shore in large numbers.

Through glasses you could see them inside the mouth of the river, appearing like hunks of ice, disappearing, reappearing. Some, swimming nearby in the water of Hudson Bay off the gravel beach were feeding on schools of fish which, when ice goes out, come in on the tides. You could hear the small whales, or belugas, in reality members of the Delphinidae or dolphin family, puffing and blowing in the stillness as they emerged for air, white glistening bodies catching the pink of early sunset. The annual arrival of the white whales (as they're always called in this area) which, in their hundreds or thousands leave again at the end of summer for no one knows exactly where, is a great event. Apparently some stay around all winter where there is open water in parts of Hudson Bay. Others have been seen off Greenland, down the Atlantic coast, and in the St. Lawrence river; from Alaska they travel to Vancouver Island and the northwest Pacific. Here, they're a valuable source of dog food, their oil and blubber are important products, and many humans, especially the natives, enjoy whale steaks.

The mouth of the Churchill River is a favorite feeding place for the animals and an excellent hunting ground for their pursuers. Early last evening a half dozen canoes with outboard engines, in the distance like black whirligig beetles, were roaring about the river hot on the chase.

Someone suggested a hike to the Merry Rocks at the tip of the Churchill Peninsula where the river mouth and whales could be watched at close quarters. Sue and I jumped at the chance and hurried to put on warmer clothes. From the depths of a crowded duffel, I fished out the violet tam presented by Horace; his latest — and oddest — gift, because it goes with my eyes, he said! Anyhow, up here one continually wears such shapeless apparel, even a little thing like a becoming tam is a sort of morale booster. From biting winds and brief periods of blazing sun, I've already acquired a very dark tan which, though not the striking red-brown of Sue's, is quite impressive.

In the company of Terence, Dr. Carey and the two young trappers, we walked several miles along the track past that ugly grain elevator, rather like a city sky-scraper dropped by mistake in the midst of an arctic waste, over loose stones and gravel, up and down across rock ledges. On top of the long miles we'd already done that day it was a bit tough, but we're feeling really fit, and at the end an enthralling sight met our eyes.

Cape Merry, consisting of small low ledges jutting out into the sea, forms a narrow little tip of the Churchill Peninsula. White whales, traveling in schools of six or eight or ten, sometimes single with a young gray one attached or swimming close to its parent, were moving silently and continuously through the quarter mile width of the river mouth. On the incoming tide they came from the calm pink and green-blue waters of Hudson Bay, white ice shining in the distance, through the river entrance to spread out in all direc-tions. As some came in others went out. It was simply hypnotizing to watch those sleek gleaming bodies —

impossible to tell head from tail except by the direction in which they traveled — arching up and down, diving in and out, rolling luxuriously across a wave, bending gracefully like bows as they came to the surface. An entire body sometimes, sinews and muscles flexing like beautiful steel, leapt half clear of the water. Sometimes only a part appeared so that the animals looked like a bit of submerged ice. Perhaps it was because they were never still and you could never see one long, or fully enough to be sure exactly what it looked like, that you wanted to watch forever those unending, delicious, graceful undulations.

On the small rocks, surrounded by water, in the hush of the radiant evening, the only sounds were the lap of waves, cries of seabirds, an ice cake swishing by, a rhythmical splash of a whale with its soothing puffs as it came up for air. Occasionally a forceful puff blew out a mist of water vapor and made a sudden weird sound.

Sometimes two whales seemed to bump together with a loud hoarse cough. "When they fight they sound like bulls," remarked Eric Grey unexpectedly at my elbow. (Except for a first hard look he hadn't appeared even to notice me before!) He has a very good voice with a British-Canadian accent, but his coloring and cast of countenance are markedly Scandinavian.

"These whales or dolphins as they are actually" — he and Mr. McIntyre are the first people we've struck up here who know this — "certainly are capable of making strange sounds," he went on in answer to my comment on the supposed lack of voice in some Cetaceans. "I've heard them myself often, as well as other kinds of whales. A couple I knew on the Gaspé coast told me once they were badly disturbed one night by a strange moaning and a sort of roaring. A sickening, haunting noise not like anything they'd ever heard — couldn't make up their minds whether it was the voice of something alive or some strange new note in wind and waves. They couldn't sleep listening to it — and when they went out next morning to the beach near their house they traced it to a Greenland whale caught between rocks and stranded there at low tide. It was found soon by fishermen and killed, of course. Otherwise possibly it would have survived and got free when the tide was high again."*

It made me sick to think of it; for these whales must be highly organized creatures, capable of great suffering. After all they're warm-blooded mammals like us, high up in the animal world.

* This observation was recounted at Churchill by Mrs. Eva Beckett to the author in July 1949. Similar instances are reported from time to time of whales, sometimes whole herds, being stranded by storms or very high tides in various parts of the world.

I asked what the people out on the river were doing with them. Mr. Grey said, "Using harpoons — sharp metal implements seven or eight inches long fastened on the end of an eight-foot pole. The poles have a hundred or so feet of rope and an empty oil can or barrel tied to the other end of the rope for a float; they go after the whales if it's calm like tonight, or early in the morning. When they get close the lad in the bow throws the harpoon. If it goes in and catches, the boat can follow the float till the whale tires or slows down. Usually they go up and shoot it, sometimes net it, then tow it to shore."

I also asked if these whales are really big enough to be valuable for oil, and he said, "A fair-sized one yields about forty-five gallons. Whales, as well as seals, are very valuable to the natives, especially Eskimos, for both food and fuel. Just about every part of the whale can be used. Meat, blood, bones, hide, everything makes a swell food for dogs and other animals. Someday they'll start a real whale factory here at Churchill and it's good-by whales unless the government puts on restrictions. . . ."

Observing my great interest and the notes I was jotting down, he kindly described the beluga in further detail. This is Mr. Grey's fourth year in the Hudson Bay region; as he's traveled over the far northwest sec-

tion around Repulse Bay, as well as on the Barrens north
of Churchill, he's hunted whales himself for dog food
and had ample opportunity to examine freshly-caught
animals.

They are beautiful and harmless creatures really, except perhaps on the very rare occasions when, chased
and unmercifully harpooned, one quite justifiably up-
sets a canoe.

The white whale's length in these parts may be anywhere from twelve to twenty feet — he thinks twelve to
fifteen is most usual. Its weight is around eleven hundred to two thousand pounds. It has a broad rudderlike
tail and on either shoulder a thick flipper possessing the
rudiments of five fingers inside the skin. There are
small, piglike eyes which must have fairly good sight
since the animals become quickly aware of moving figures on land or water. The ears, tiny holes on either
side of the head, are apparently capable of keen hear-
ing, and are able to sense with great quickness current
and water vibrations. Whales can swim easily and safely
all around dangerous, submerged rocks and shoals in
the dark.

The animal posseses small teeth which are the typical
conical shape of toothed whales to which dolphins belong. There is a single spiracle or blowhole, the only
nostril, on top of the head. This leads directly to the

lungs and is unconnected with the mouth, as air ducts
are in land mammals. Otherwise the lungs would be
filled with water. The blowhole is closed by valves
when the whale submerges, and it must be brought to
the surface at regular intervals, about every ten or fifteen minutes, to refill the lungs with air. Just as the
animal reaches the surface, air is expelled with ex-
plosive force to empty the lungs so they can be refilled
the instant mouth and nostril are out of water. What
sometimes looks like a spout of water is the warm breath
condensing in cold air. Mr. Grey says he's seen big
whales off the coast of Greenland make a cloud so
dense that for a few minutes it obscured all the land
behind them.

No one seems to know much about the beluga's mat-
ing or family habits. "You couldn't chase a whale
around the seas much for observation!" But he supposed
these are like other members of the whale group in
having usually one young about every other year (the
gestation period is said to be ten or twelve months).
Some of the natives here have seen an embryo in a
white whale around May or June. Milk glands are on
the abdomen, and the mother whale is said to roll somewhat on one side and bring the rear of her body to the
surface, so that the young can nurse with the nostril
out of water.

The belugas have a terrifically strong, tough, white hide with a great layer underneath of pink blubber, sometimes ten inches thick, protecting all the vital organs in the most icy water; probably the animals live on this when they can't get sufficient food. It's the blubber which is so valuable for the oil it contains. "Back in old Sam Hearne's day," he finished, "it was said in successful years they shipped home to England eight to thirteen tons of whale oil from Churchill. Like to go whale hunting some day? Sure I'll take you!"

It had become a more and more perfect summer's evening, seeming to hold all the earth in warmth and tranquility. The smooth sky, again so vast and unimpeded that one seemed lost in it, drowned in it, unlike that first night of flaming clouds, grew to a deeper, warmer pink and apricot shading into every lovely delicacy of cream and lavender. The water of sea and river, still, except for the ripples of waves and whales, turned apricot with bands of turquoise and darker amethyst. Ice floes in the distance were yellow and salmon shading imperceptibly into the salmon and gold horizon. The air was balmy as a spring night at home, only the rare breath of ice reminding you that this was indeed the very Far North. The rocks against which we leaned, still warm at ten P.M., were bathed in a glow of brilliant twilight.

We had all grown completely quiet, silenced by the color, the serene vastness of sky and water, the rhythmic splashings. Inspired by Eric Grey's remark on the days of Samuel Hearne we were looking just across the river toward the opposite shore where faint gray lines of wall appeared; all that is left now of the ruins of famous old Fort Prince of Wales.

After a time Dr. Carey, who is something of an authority on early Canadian history, spoke in that quiet, rather shy, dreamy sort of manner of his:

"Maybe it was just this kind of evening away back in 1782 when old Sam Hearne, Governor of the Hudson's Bay Company at Churchill, and his men looked out from their walls over there and suddenly saw three great French warships commanded by Admiral La Pérouse. They hadn't even known there were any ships on all the 400,000 square miles of Hudson Bay or seen signs of one, anymore than we have this year. They didn't even know war had broken out between England and France. Must have been quite a shock, especially when they found there were four hundred armed Frenchmen against their thirty-nine."

For Sue's and my special benefit, he described the fort which once had been considered so impregnable. Started in 1731 by the H.B.C. to protect their trade from rival companies, it wasn't actually completed till 1771.

After that there hadn't been a sign of an enemy for eleven years. Built in a square about three hundred feet on each side with a V bastion at each corner, it was like a four-point star. The outer wall of stone blocks was eighteen feet high and within it, earth and stone ramparts were held secure by another stone retaining wall, making a total thickness of some forty feet around the whole fort. On top of all this was a six-foot stone parapet to protect the gunners. There were forty cannons on the ramparts and a battery of six cannons across the river on this side of the harbor entrance. It was supposed to be foolproof against attack.

"Seems funny, don't it," remarked Terence, our Irishman; "a man of old Hearne's reputation giving in to the French like that without any sort of fight even?"

"What else could he do?" asked Dr. Carey, "with thirty-nine men against four hundred and things around the fort more or less out of repair? The French seized the wonderful stores of furs, burned the buildings, and sailed off with Hearne a prisoner. Later La Pérouse, who must have been a man of discernment, got in touch with the authorities in England and required that Sam Hearne's journal, still today one of our best sources of early information on exploration in the Northland, including observations on natural history, be published as part of Hearne's ransom. . . . Anyhow the prestige of the old fort over there was gone forever and after the war the H.B.C. re-established their trading post up the river on their old original site in Munck's Cove."

"Why Munck's Cove?" Sue asked. "Is that the building you see across the river beyond the Anglican church?" This and another small place some distance east, called Denny's, appear to be the only human habitations on the edge of a vast wilderness stretching for endless miles across the Barrenlands.

Churchill was first discovered, Dr. Carey said, in 1619 by Jens Munck, son of a Danish nobleman, in that period when everyone was looking for a northwest passage. Munck and his party sailing down the flat west coastline of Hudson Bay saw a deep break and rocky headlands and hoped, as so many others had, that they'd found it. They were obliged to winter near the tidal mouth of the big river — a party of sixty-one (Danes, Norwegians, and two Englishmen); all but Munck himself and two others died of scurvy. The survivors went back next year to Europe and never returned to Hudson Bay.

And in those days, just as they do now, wonderful cranberries, one of the best of antiscorbutics, grew around them in masses. Hudson Bay later became famous for its cranberries. Great quantities of them packed in barrels of moist sugar were shipped across to England.

In about 1688, explorers of the Hudson's Bay Company rediscovered this great river and named it for Sir John Churchill, governor of the company and later the Duke of Marlborough. But it wasn't till 1717 that the H.B. established a permanent post in the spot where Munck spent that terrible winter.

The present, very aged little Anglican church near the post was brought out in those days in sections by ship from England and played a big part in the life up here. It was used for religious meetings and a class room for Indians on weekdays. Each summer, even now, Indians still camp around it to receive their treaty money — about five dollars per person paid yearly by the Canadian government.

At home we're all rather indifferent to mail. So much of it so often, I suppose. Now we can hardly wait for the weekly train. Do hope there's something from the family. But definitely I'm not homesick! Doing work you love in such a setting (even if it has tough moments) is a never-ending thrill. I'm not much alarmed anymore of being off by myself in the tent (I *was* petrified at first). And I've never felt better in my life. I doubt if there's a healthier climate anywhere.

July

Four

ꙮꙮꙮꙮꙮꙮꙮꙮꙮꙮꙮꙮꙮꙮꙮꙮꙮꙮꙮꙮꙮ

J ULY has come, but here it seems more like a crisp, brilliant spring than the hot, languid midsummer of New England. It's wonderful to wake to rose-filled, crystal mornings and the ripplings and tinklings of the birds. Bubbling music of longspurs and achingly sweet notes of white-crowned sparrows last till eleven P.M. and begin again at 1:30 or 2 A.M. Some of the birds sing all night. And now there is that new and thrilling sound which I hear right from my bed — the luscious puffing and blowing and splashing of white whales just off the gravel beach.

After the very cold, storm-tossed days we've lately been passing, these last few nights, so clear and still, have been utterly restful and luxurious. Gales sweeping over Churchill lashed the canvas and stovepipe so violently that I was certain my very exposed living quarters, and I with them, would take off on Hudson Bay. But everything, exactly according to Terry's reassurances, held firm, though whirls of icy, stinging rain poured through the canvas on sections drawn tight against the boards. I was thankful for Bill's large rubber sheet to cover the bunk, certain shrunken portions of his old wool underwear (masculine things do seem so much more effective in the rough life than their feminine equivalents), and occasional fires in the tiny stove. Since I've grasped the scarcity of fuel around Churchill, however, and watched my own rapidly dwindling woodpile — which Terry assured me would be replenished but it never has — I light few fires and use the stove in Sue's shack, where we spend considerable time anyway.

Sue's shack is the weirdest mixture of dead and alive birds and animals, rotten eggs being prepared for the collection, all sorts of skinning paraphernalia and preservatives, guns and nets, wet clothes, bedding, odd bits of food. I thank God daily for my comparatively retired and spacious tent. Sue, happily, is far less squeamish and infinitely more hospitable. How she ever puts up with all of us dashing in and out and using her one room as a sort of way station, I can't imagine.

On very stormy days she and I eat there — a light lunch of ptarmigan breasts (quite heavenly delicious like tender, remarkably tasty chicken) from the collection of ptarmigans she and Dr. S. are making. We cook them on Sue's tiny stove; then eat them on the one shelf-and-table combination amid bird skins and feathers, a wash basin of evil-smelling egg yolks, dead lemmings, soap and toilet articles, toothbrush and toothpaste, and deadly poisons in the way of arsenic. Nothing impairs the appetites, at least, of either of us.

With infinite labor, one rainy day, the basin being temporarily emptied of egg contents, we each took a shampoo there. It's a blessing we both have short plain hair (though what with lack of washing and perpetual headgear, we've given up trying to maintain the well-groomed caps we ordinarily aspire to). There are neither running water nor toilet facilities in Churchill. Everyone carries pails from the nearest tap connected with a pipeline which brings water from Lake Rosabelle. Sewage has to be emptied in back yards or on the rocks. This doesn't appear to present any problem. Perhaps the dogs are good scavengers; anyway it's so cold and so much boisterous wind rushes about that there're never any bad smells, rather a delightful impression of perpetual freshness and cleanliness.

Terry, whose last name we have learned only recently is Casey, has the most slipshod habits and can be the most exasperating person. And we all love him to distraction. As who around Churchill — except a few prominent evildoers — does not? No one can resist that heartening Irish warmth, the startling penetration of those small blue eyes nearly hidden by triangular lids, eyebrows like a bush, that wild white thatch, the way he wrinkles the Cyrano de Bergerac nose, and tosses back his head when something strikes his funny bone, which it does a hundred times a day. There are also his profound knowledge of the North and apparent ability to deal with life in its various phases. He came to this country as a small child, with his parents, from Donegal. They lived in a log cabin in Saskatchewan and much of his boyhood was spent trapping with his father and Indians in the flat, forest country. All sorts of people keep coming to the café, not as I at first supposed for the food which is poor, even taking into account the difficulty of obtaining supplies, but for the cheering comfort he gives and his generally wise advice.

And he is a poet! He has a small notebook full of verses — mostly on wild, adventurous, stormy themes, not at all grammatical sometimes, but now and then with a feeling for beauty and atmosphere that's both stirring and touching.

I'm grateful especially for Terry's tactful care of my welfare. Each evening I go to the café for a nightly kettle of hot water to carry back to the tent. Half of it fills a hot water bottle for my very damp, cold sleeping bag, half a basin for a bath. Usually there're strange men talking or playing cards in the café and I hate to go in, but Terry makes everyone else feel as easy and natural as he is. While we wait for water to heat he regales me with fascinating tales, or eggs on the other men to talk. And when they really get going, I just sit there openmouthed until midnight —

I don't know exactly what I'd pictured these Northerners would be — men of action and resourcefulness and great adventure certainly. I hadn't realized what deep thinkers and philosophers they all — illiterate as well as literate — are besides. Even in the toughest of them, not religious obviously from the viewpoint of a churchgoer and the generally accepted sense, you somehow get a feeling of spiritual values and knowledge of something far beyond the purely material. Like all those who know the real things, these men are *big*, with a complete sort of simplicity and unpretentiousness.

Most of them, especially the trappers, spend long periods — many months of each year apparently — entirely alone. A good deal of their life must be sordid and rough and full of privations, yet they have time to observe beauty and to think, endlessly — on every subject under the sun. They see things from their contact with man's world and civilization where part of their life is spent. And they see things from their contact with a world which is not of man at all; where all the forces of a wilderness and the universe itself are predominant. Each man if he has come safely through several years in the North is truly self-sufficient, for he must have learned how to guard both body and soul. What his standards toward fellow mortals and other living things may be depends, I suppose, on the individual. But if these are not good on the whole, could he survive for long?

While the men discuss and listen to each other (and during the tallest tales — they all sound tall — cast sidelong glances at me), we all drink endless cups of bedtime tea. No one up here drinks anything else; if you go on a round of visiting you have to be a bottomless well to absorb the quarts and quarts so hospitably urged upon you.

Incidentally the silent young man, Terry's café partner, is "Luke," and very nice he is. He continues to be more or less consistently speechless and he has a cast in one eye, but he is a dear and very dependable. I think he holds the café business together, in a self-effacing way, when he isn't engaged in some job at the elevator docks.

Luke is the only person we've seen up here who wears glasses. The clearness and depth of eyes of people in this part of the world are especially noticeable. Though they read a great deal (and not by bright electric lights either), they're forever looking at vast distances and

using vision and eye muscles as these were intended
to be used.

Besides the trappers there are, occasionally, groups of
railroad workers to whom Terry and Luke serve a huge
nightly meal. We've eaten with them several times —
and I sort of love them. Their clothes and faces often
are rather black, but their hands are clean. Rarely
there's a talker among them; mostly, except for "Pass
the bread" and "Thanks," they eat in steady and utter
silence, stocking up exhausted bodies with Terry's enormous thick platefuls of potatoes and baked beans, eggs
and ham or some unrecognizable meat, mountains of
bread, gallons of black tea. There is none of the
sprightly conversation so invariably the conventional
necessary accompaniment to meals in our world. The
bodies of these men may be tired but their nerves and
minds are quiet and at ease. You feel rested just sitting
there with them, and I can get comfortably and un-
consciously through a platterful of food, a quarter of
whose size would kill me dead at home.

Then there is Ellie, a Chipewyan girl, who does
sewing and washing for Terry in return for his kind
deeds to her and her family — bringing them caribou
and seal he has hunted, helping her once when she
was very sick. She appears frequently, a darling small
papoose hung on her back. The little boards to which

all these snugly wrapped Indian babies are attached, look like a wonderful idea. They must produce very straight, strong backs and the baby can be placed safely and comfortably anywhere — on its mother's shoulders, on the ground, hung up on a pole, and so on. I've tried to make friends with Ellie but she doesn't speak English, and from the hostile way she eyes me and from Terry's shrugs and suppressed chuckles, I uncomfortably and indignantly suspect that she takes me for a newly-acquired, licentious part of Terry's establishment!

I'm beginning to have not infrequent gentlemen callers. I shortly recovered from qualms about men coming into the tent; though I was a bit startled the first time two walked in one morning and sat themselves down in the middle of my unmade bed. But we do exactly the same when we visit the trappers' tents. (After all there is no other place to sit.) By special invitation we've been to see acquaintances of Terry's; and the abode of Mr. Grey and Mr. McIntyre — a tent slightly newer and more retired than most. Up here, the space within four walls be it tent or one-room shack, is the place where you sleep, carry on private affairs, or entertain, all with equal abandon.

Introductions are a rarity. Except as a necessary mark of identification, names mean little. It's not who you are, famous or infamous, good or bad elsewhere, but what you are right here in one of the least trammeled lands on earth. People seldom bother with my name. (How this would distress dear Father!) Even if they thought it were illustrious it wouldn't signify in the least. They're only mildly interested in what I'm doing. Many odd people, from odd parts of the world, drift here to do odd things. It's me, what I have inside, that matters; with a few exceptions I doubt whether feminine charm has much to do with likes or dislikes, obligingness or lack of it. They look inside you and in their quite friendly, but definitely reserved way, decide whether you have guts, genuineness, dependability. If they think so they may do anything for you, if they don't they won't.

When I have visitors Terry seems to know which are desirables, and which are not, appearing on errands when the latter turn up and remaining till he carries them off with him. A certain Dutch Hans, "Dutchy," one of the tougher trappers, has developed a most uncomfortable yen for me, coming to the tent at odd times with candy and lurid magazines. When he squeezes my arm and mutters "keed" it takes careful maneuvering to escape with tact. But of all the men, nice, tough, or indifferent, that I've come in contact with thus far, Dutchy is the only one of this sort. Occasionally I've had refreshing encounters with my old train pal Duncan Scott and one or two with Slim Jim, but not that attractive Scotsman who took my fancy the first day on the dinkey. Though Churchill's so small a place no one seems to know of him and, in typical northern fashion, apparently he's dropped out of sight.

Definitely among the desirables is one Father Pierre, a French-Canadian priest from the mission nearby, who stops by my tent or the café for occasional chats. His dark hair and eyes and finely-chiseled features are strikingly good-looking; his wit and observations on life as he finds it in extensive missions and adventures through the Arctic are positively enthralling. Some tragic family affair drove him from the highly cultured, social world to which he seems obviously to belong, into the priesthood and to this terrifically tough and lonely life. But like everyone else we've met so far who has come to the North — and remained — he seems to possess that strangely deep feeling for it.

There's beauty, he says, and romance! And wonderful health and strength in this kind of life. The Arctic teaches you things you never learn anywhere else. You just plain like it — sometimes love it very greatly — sometimes you never want to see it again and wonder why you stick it when you're frozen in a storm and the pain of your body is bigger than anything else on earth, or when something goes horribly, terribly wrong. . . .

"Like the time I had to amputate a woman's leg in a post way north of here. . . . No one else to do it, no way of getting in help or getting her out. It was winter; she'd been mangled by a starving dog (gone too close to it or something). Her husband was the Mountie. He'd had some medical training just as we're supposed to have. Supposed to be able to handle a childbirth, perform an appendectomy, amputate limbs, and so on . . . Anyway my amputation was all right, but we didn't have enough of the right implements and drugs. She died — of bleeding and shock. . . ."

One day when I expressed a wish that I could stay for longer than these summer months, he said, "What's to prevent you then? What difference would twelve months more make to your studies at the university or your family in comparison with what you'd gain from this world?"

"And just how would I convince my family or the university of this?"

"Take a boat in August to some point north of here, don't catch it on the return trip. They'd send a message out you missed the boat! Chances are there's no other way to get out till breakup next year. You've *got* to stay! You wouldn't be the first who's done that either!"

He's offered to take me with him when he goes way

up to Chesterfield Inlet or some place and leave me there. I believe he'd do it too. So — if I don't turn up this fall. . . . He invited me to go to the Catholic mission house to visit the bishop who's all covered with black whiskers, but "not bad underneath, and great fun — "

I find it difficult sometimes to believe Father Pierre *is* a priest at all (at least the priest of my preconceived ideas). But each time he's departing, for a sudden surprising instant he transforms from one vast, wicked twinkle into something grave and stern as he makes the sign of the cross over me. Descendant of liberal Unitarian generations, I find this invariably startling.

There is also the earnest young minister, Mr. Esmond, with a decided mind of his own, from the United Church where Dr. Stevens and the Canadians sleep. I've had more than one stimulating conversation with him on English literature. Fancy finding people up here who quote Browning. "But," as Sue says, bringing me up short as frequently happens, "whyever not?" I greatly fear sometimes that I'm not one whit better than those narrow members of the family I'm always criticizing. I've got an awful lot to learn. Like all the church officials here, Guy Esmond somehow doesn't look the part; he's lean and weatherbeaten and hard, and always wears hip boots. The Anglican minister, except for a clerical collar, is the same. They're all far more typical of the North somehow than of the church. I think the North leaves a mark on all that she touches; a mark so indelible it's stronger than any other.

Five

~~~~~~~~~~~~~~~~~~~~~~~~~~~~~~~~~~~~~

J ULY 3RD. Owing to the recent storms, we've been confined lately to points near Churchill. But now each day since the evening excursion to Cape Merry has *dawned* (whatever else it's turned into later), calm and sparkling, and each morning we've been off again for long hours in the vicinity of Lakes Isabelle and Rosabelle and the timberline beyond.

The tundra has bloomed. That first day after the big storm when we got off the dinkey and looked around, we all cried out. Overnight a miracle had happened. The whole wide world was alive with brilliant color. Great waves of rose and magenta, white and gold, spread in every direction as far as the eye could see. The little *Rhododendron lapponicium* stretched carpets of vivid rose all across the earth. Huge fluffy clusters of white Labrador tea, both *Ledum groenlandicum* and *L. palustre,* and pink delicate bells of bog rosemary, *Andromeda polifolia,* transformed every mossy mound

[78]

into a giant's embroidered pin cushion. There were
great gardens of little, white, starlike saxifrages, *Saxifraga tricuspidata,* growing on red stems out of sharp,
awl-like leaves, graceful white grass-of-Parnassus, gold-
en buttercups, tiny, exquisite, rose and lavender round-
leaved orchids, *Orchis rotundifolia,* less conspicuous
flowers of the cress and mustard family. Whole glades
and flat areas were covered with the big, pink, single
roselike flower of the arctic raspberry, *Rubus arcticus;*
or the white, gold-centered *Rubus chamaemorus* whose
golden fruits later in the season are alike delectable to
wild things and humans. Flat magenta cushions of
Saxifraga oppositifolia were scattered everywhere along
gravel outcrops; much of it was already over since it is
probably the earliest of tundra flowers to bloom here.
(I'm using scientific names not just to pay Bill back
for all those archaeological things, but because many
of the plants here don't have common English names;
also I want the scientific ones for future reference.)

Little prostrate, foot-high arctic willows spread everywhere in masses, had become a paradise for humming
bees and tiny butterflies; the upright, inch-long, fluffy,
flowering spikelike heads of the many different species
turned, according to shades of pistil or stamen with
which each plant is adorned, gold, orange, pink, deep
red, or a crimson so dark it looked black. For in the

manner of all dioecious members of the willow family, the sexes instead of being combined in each flower as in the cases of higher members of the botanical world, are on separate plants — one plant bearing all the male flowers, another, not far away, having the female; depending on winds and insects for cross-fertilization and the continuance of existence.

That first day after the storm I found a stilt sand-piper's nest with three young in it. Stopping to catch the thousand bird calls underfoot and overhead, I'd been listening with particular delighted amusement to the stilt's nasal, donkeylike "hee-haw, hee-haw, hee-haw" ending in the musical trill. And then a parent stilt, almost at my feet, left the tiny imperceptible hollow of its nest, so frantic it flew straight at my ankles and hit them. It dragged its wings and teetered on those long, spindly legs which on land look comically twice as high as they ought to be for the stilt's small brown-streaked body. (When the bird wades and feeds in water, how-ever, it has a conspicuous advantage over the shorter legged shore birds — just as the wearer of hip boots has it all over someone with short ones.) You couldn't tell whether it was the male or female, for here in the sand-piper families, apparently males, even more than fe-males, care for nest and young.

That bird, twenty times over, risked its life to protect

its offspring. Two babies remained on the nest; as soon as I sat down and grew still, the parent, quivering and trembling with fright, returned and cuddled them, calling all the while in heart-rending tones upon the other. And this too came running back and crawled under, twinkling black eyes and fluffy tiny head peering out between the feathers. These babies, like all the other sandpiper young we've seen, are darlings — a warm, rufous-brown covered with polka dots of white cotton. Animated balls of fluff, they are borne about on two long, unsteady sticks.

After the stilt discovery I continued on to the clump of small wind-tossed spruce mixed with vivid green of tiny larches, where the home of the hoary redpolls is located. Ten feet above ground was the tiny nest, compactly and beautifully made of twigs and dried grasses, deeply lined with little soft gray and white feathers. No precocial young here, rather altricial which must be tenderly guarded until they can care for themselves.

A small flock of redpolls was all around the vicinity, darting in and out, reminding one exactly of goldfinches with their wavy flight and merry notes. Behind another small tree, twelve feet away, I could watch the nest and set up the Leica on a branch. In an amazingly short time, fifteen minutes to be exact, the little female which had flown from the nest, came back and settled down again on the four tiny young, cradling them carefully under wings and breast.

You never saw such a pretty sight. There was the never ending dome of blue crystal sky and the colors of flowers so fresh and newly-born, laid like brilliant quilts on the soft waves of tundra. There was the quality of the air which makes one feel so deeply and radiantly alive. And close at hand was the black-green patch of spruce with morning light centering on the deep rose cap of the little redpoll, her bright gentle eyes, the black chin spot, the prettily streaked brown and white of the wings and small body about five inches long — the size of a small warbler; only an inch or two bigger than a tiny hummingbird.

Several times when my hand moved on the camera the redpoll flew, but came back very soon to go on composedly with her housekeeping; and every time she returned with insect larvae, which she regurgitated to place in the red gaping mouths, each mouth so wide it looked as big as the rest of the whole baby bird put together. The redpoll always cleaned out most carefully any fresh, moist, white pellets of excrement, either carrying them away or swallowing them whole. How *can* the birds do this, I always wonder! But somehow it's never really revolting because the birds themselves are so clean and healthy and natural about it all.

After the cleaning and feeding, the redpoll would turn round and round, shake her feathers, fuss and fidget, before she could get herself and all the babies settled exactly right again. Then her head would droop and her bright eyes close for a nap, refreshing after such exertions.

When this had gone on for an hour or so and I'd taken several pictures, suddenly the little bird's head jerked upright, her eyes opened wide, and she began to quiver and flutter and tremble. What in the world ailed her now? She was listening to something — There was a great twittering and ecstatic warbling of goldfinchlike notes up overhead; and then a little male hoary redpoll, so perfectly beautiful I gasped, darted down to light on the branch beside the nest, his mouth crammed with tidbits. No wonder his ladylove fell into a flutter at the merest hint of his approach.

I'd been wondering about the differences, supposed to be far from distinct, between the common redpoll and the hoary, both of which species are found here at Churchill. But with that beautifully-marked male, it was plain. The white rump patch above the tail, unlike that of the common redpoll, is unstreaked. The lovely breast, all suffused with deep rose, instead of plain white or pale pink as in the female, and the coloring of his whole body, was noticeably and exquisitely all sort of frosted over with white.

Twittering and talking, black eyes twinkling, he sat beside his excited lady and neatly dropped in her mouth a delicate morsel. This he repeated four times, and when a tiny head came up under her breast, he popped the remainder in the open mouth and flew off.

I had utterly forgotten the camera! And was simply sunk, thinking I'd never have another chance for a picture like that. But I lingered still, for the female, after composing herself and smoothing ruffled feathers, now fed three of her babies out of her own mouth. And in a short time the male was back (I knew of his approach way ahead this time), approximately the same performance occurred, and I got a picture.

The morning was far along when I finally tore myself away. I had time only to glance at, instead of watch as I'd hoped, a black-poll warbler's nest in another spruce clump. This tiny black-capped bird weighing scarcely an ounce, is still another of the world's great travelers. It goes to Venezuela or even farther south every single winter, traveling at least 10,000 miles each year to and from its far northern nesting grounds.

It was very hot and mosquitoes were increasingly prominent. This pest has been kept in abeyance by the stormy weather, but when I knelt in the still, bright sunshine to gloat over and take close-ups of an exquisite flower-decked mound of tundra, a roaring cloud, so dense it shut out the whole world, suddenly enveloped me. Things like red sparks were in my ears and eyes, down my neck and back, up wrists and arms. The Leica rolled over in mud, gloves and hat splashed in a pool, things flew out of the knapsack, while I leapt about trying to get on a head net and the jacket I'd just thrown off. I've *never* felt anything like it. From tropical experiences I'd fondly thought I knew what mosquitoes were, and never heeded tales of these northern horrors which breed in the countless numbers of still pools made by melting ice each summer. Tropical insects are few in number, and pale and languid by comparison; these things are just filled with that vim and vigor which characterizes everything of the North.

Now, I implicitly believe a tale recounted in the café the other night. Workmen going down the long, straight track on a handcar one summer's day, saw in the distance a black cloud of smoke. It was not time for the weekly train; supposing an unscheduled one was coming, they hastily hauled the car off the track. The smoke came no nearer; they proceeded on their way again; it turned out to be merely an unusually extensive mob of mosquitoes —

Incidentally Bill's disreputable felt hat, which just for fun I threw in the duffel at the last minute, is proving a treasured possession. A big brim to keep out broiling sun and hold the head net off one's face is essential.

Deafened and blinded by mosquitoes which continued to slip up inside the head net and had to be shaken out every so often, weighed down by hip boots, heavy clothes, glasses and camera, I finally staggered on toward a great open stretch of tundra where Mr. Clayton had located a nest of the parasitic jaeger. And before I even saw him, bumped nearly into a khaki-clad figure bent over camera and tripod, practically invisible under a head net and black swarms of insects. A familiar chuckle issued forth:

"Well, Rosy," said Dr. Stevens, "how's it going? Not so rosy now, eh?"

I said, "I never felt anything so fiendish anywhere. Why, if anyone got stuck or chained up or something out here they'd go really crazy."

"I'm crazy right now!" said he grimly.

He was pleased to hear about the experience with the redpolls and delighted over the stilt sandpiper's nest since only one other has been found and the eggs in it unaccountably destroyed.

That very evening he brought back one of the baby stilts in his pocket to the café. We put it on the table and it hopped all over the place; it landed in my plate of baked beans, and was a fascinating addition to our supper hour. Though Mr. Clayton, whose insides war continually with these heavy starchy diets (dyspepsia seems so incongruous with his huge and ruddy frame), had bloodthirsty designs on it and wished he could eat it instead of the beans. Beans and potatoes, tea, bread, and oatmeal seem to form the chief diet here. Occasionally this is lightened by fresh fish, caribou meat, and eggs; or a salad and ice cream gotten in on the weekly train. Green vegetables don't appear at all. Most people have gotten on healthily so long without them, probably they wouldn't especially want them even if they could get them.

The baby stilt was destined, alas, for a specimen. Dr. S. and Sue are collecting a series of young shore birds; little is known about these northern species. But I'm glad my job with birds this summer doesn't involve collecting and is to be confined largely to photography and writing up observations.

I lingered in Dr. Stevens's locality as long as possible. He has more worth-while general knowledge of this country than all the rest of our party put together. He's the keenest observer too. We all find nests and things but Dr. S. really locates the big majority. It's sad he has to depart so soon to get back to the university, and that I couldn't leave home when Sue did and thus missed all those first weeks with him.

I watched the phalaropes, little plovers, and sandpipers he was photographing around the sandy shores of a small pond. Northern phalaropes are particularly common up here. These dainty little shore birds with their neat, compact bodies, lobed feet, and sandpiper-like bills, their exquisite coloring — dark backs with dark gray, or almost black, over head and hind neck, white throat patch, brick red and ocher down sides of the neck — are the most distinctive, charming little creatures. They dart about on the water and twirl around as rapidly as water beetles, flying up swiftly when alarmed, as swiftly settling on the surface again, light as fluffs of thistledown, so softly they hardly make a ripple. Scarcely as large as our robin, the phalaropes in the fall migrate far out to sea, following plankton, on which they feed, over the north and south Atlantic. Oddly enough for the bird world, the female phalaropes are the more brightly colored, aggressive ones who have all the good times. They even do the courting and, except for actually laying eggs, gad flippantly about enjoying life, while the good, steady, efficient little husbands do all the real chores of incubating and caring for nest and young.

This is a man's world all right. Male birds, as well as

male humans, appear to be the most important members of a community. They even do the housework.

Near the edge of the big sweep of tundra I sank down in the last small tree clump to eat and rest (if such a thing were possible). If you keep perfectly still you are more mosquitoproof, even though they gather in mats outside a head net and their roar drowns out other sounds. I would take time out to nap for just a few minutes (this is easier to do in this air than anywhere I've ever been), and I was drifting off when a hoarse, indignant "Tut, tut, tut, tut, tut," started me bolt upright. I looked around guiltily: Dr. Stevens of course. . .

And then, "You wretched thing," I said to a willow ptarmigan strutting pompously on softly feathered feet out of the tree clump and eying me indignantly. It has some amazingly human notes, this small arctic grouse; and despite its ridiculously tame behavior is most comical and pretty to look upon, its body mottled in grays and tans and black just like a live piece of tundra, the bright-red skin patch above the big shining dark eye, the white wings. In winter, except for black on the tail and a black line through the eye, it turns pure white and becomes invisible against a snowdrift. When Sue and Dr. S. arrived in late May the ptarmigan still bore bits of their white winter plumage, just as bits of snowdrifts still lay scattered all across the tundra. Ptarmigan, so numerous and tame and easy to kill, form an important food item in the diet of natives and white trappers in this country.

The white dot which marked the jaeger blind was a mile or so away. There were not even tiny trees on this particular big sweep of tundra which stretched straight out to Hudson Bay and was marked on its southern extremity by the gravel ridge and arms of timberline. It seemed unusually wet (though what region here is not with ice a mere few feet below surface melting in every direction); there were few dry hummocks and flower carpets were scarce. Dark clouds had risen, and a stiff breeze considerably lessened the mosquito menace. It all looked wild and utterly bleak again. But the little ponds and shores were swarming with birds — sandpipers (the beautiful red-backed with their purplish-brown backs and black bellies were also here), phalaropes, golden plovers, old-squaws, pintails, and dowitchers with their long, straight bills and lovely buff-colored underparts. Apparently no one yet has ever photographed the dowitcher on its nest.*
Bonaparte gulls and arctic terns screamed raucously overhead; there was the winnowing noise

* In 1944, at Churchill, Dr. A. A. Allen obtained probably the first photo of this species on its nest.

of Wilson's snipe, the wild incessant calling of curlews.

I walked for more than a mile, plodding across mucky
ground and, because I was exhausted from skirting
endlessly around them, plunging recklessly through
stretches of water whose bottoms sank alarmingly, before I heard a new voice — like a red-shouldered hawk
with a gull-like timbre. The jaegers at last. Thank
goodness, they were there and must be guarding the
nest. A pair began circling overhead like large, dark,
hawklike gulls, the two elongated tail feathers and
flashes of white on the wings showing plainly. Jaegers,
belonging actually to the Skua family, are classed as
falconlike sea birds. They swooped down; one, with
terrific suddenness, dived directly on me. You could
hear the swish, and wind from powerful wings fanned
my face; something grazed my head sharply. I hit at it
and cowered to earth. Gosh! If one struck hard it
would tear your head open. (The Eskimos say this bird
once attacked human beings, killed, and ate them!)
Now the calls and screams seemed to verge on a cat-
like, distressed mewing and, while one continued to
dive, and I crouched down each time despite a firm
resolve not to, the other with fierce, wild eyes lit on the
ground and tried desperately, with dragged wings and
tail, to decoy me away. It was the most thrilling and

intimate experience I've ever had with such a furious big bird.

I was thankful to get safely inside the shelter of the tiny blind. The nest, about eight feet away, was a hollowed space in a great cushion of bright, yellow-green moss; one of the two, big, olive-gray, splotched eggs had hatched (there had been two eggs the evening before), and there was a gray fuzzy baby like a young duck, wobbling about on pink webbed feet.

The hummock with the nest was surrounded by water; the blind was standing in oozy muck and it was impossible to rest one's aching legs by sitting down. Because of hip boots I could kneel, however, for short periods. In about twenty minutes one of the jaegers approached, the young bird which had been crouched by the unhatched egg began to call, and the big bird lit almost on the edge of the nest. But even as I cautiously began to move the camera at the little opening in the blind, the jaeger was up again. This happened three times; twice the jaeger settled on the nest but was off before a picture could be snapped. One of my sleeping feet was simply excruciating and time was passing.

It's amazing how time does pass when you're off on your own on the tundra. You are never lonely a second. Hours fly by like minutes and there is simply never a dull instant. No day is ever a quarter long enough to

observe things and accomplish what you want to. Out
in the field at least there is no such thing as a "bored
naturalist."

Finally the mother bird (I supposed) settled and
stayed, though she looked keenly toward the blind with
angry black eyes. The shape of the bill and body
seemed more than ever like a big dark gull, but the
long pointed tail feathers and plumply-curving, beautifully soft white breast, contrasting with the dark back,
were distinctive. The young bird had wandered down
off the side of the hummock, now plucking at leaves and
grasses for food, now taking short naps, head sunk on
breast. It was a precocial young, but obviously too
weak and newly hatched to stand much exertion. The
parent, apparently satisfied that danger from the blind
was past, with a completely new, surprisingly tender
note, began now to call for it. Her black, fierce eyes
were incredibly softened to a liquid dark brown. Fascinated, I watched that whole terrifyingly wild demeanor
transform to a touching gentleness and tenderness. The
little one struggled back up beside its mother's breast
and reached up to touch her bill. The big bird looked
lovingly down upon it, but made no attempt to feed it
or gather it under her body.

The jaeger gobbled up quantities of mosquitoes from
where she sat. Various other birds — ducks, plovers, etc.

— do the same. Though I hate to consider such an idea, perhaps even mosquitoes are useful enough to form an important part in the scheme of things. At least they must help protect a wilderness from the ravages of man.

Once after the parent had flown off and come back again, I took a wonderful picture as she lit with great wings still outspread. Several times the male came and stood on top of the blind and its weight made the canvas sink down right on top of my head. Really something to have a jaeger standing on your head quite unconscious of what he was resting upon! You could see the big, dark webbed feet through the cloth; I reached up and gently lifted the bird, and still supposing my hand to be just part of the blind, he didn't fly.

Once the male lit on the nest directly beside the sitting female with the young bird crouched at her breast, and looked proudly down upon them, and I got (I hope) a picture which will take your breath away.

When I left the jaegers, after twice sitting down in muck because what with pins and needles I couldn't stand up, blazing sun and mosquitoes were out again full force. I'd decided that morning instead of returning on the dinkey, to hike back on my own along the Rock Ridge to Churchill. So I headed diagonally toward Hudson Bay which, in the clear light, looked barely half a mile distant. It turned out, of course, to be at least three times as far, but when I reached it —

A cool, brisk wind and sweet salt tang from the bay caused all but a bearable few mosquitoes to vanish. A small rise, an opening in the Rock Ridge a quarter mile wide, just like a summer lawn of vivid green, sloped down in dense waving carpets of avens, *Dryas integrifolia,* not yet quite in bloom, to the soft, intense, afternoon blue of the sea. Left and right, mossy outcrops winding up between great gray or reddish-yellow rock masses, were lined with the brilliant rose and pink and gold of dwarf rhododendron, tiny alpine azaleas, *Loiseleuria procumbens,* and arctic willows. It was a new enchanting world, utterly unlike the great wild tundra sweeps below, yet still with that same untouched, untamed quality and hidden strength of arctic places.

Following the flower-filled, mossy ways, I climbed left up to the rocks which run north along the bay toward Churchill. All along the way deep hollows and crevices held winding, narrow, little fresh water pools, three to five feet deep. Exquisite bathtubs of clear water warmed by sun and reflections from the rocks, far less icy than ponds and lakes of the tundra. Each pool against the larkspur-blue background of Hudson Bay, was a mirror of light blue sky, red and gray rock, rose and purple and green of flowering plants and leaves and lichens which fringed its margins. Little white heather bells and pearly pink Pyrolas were commoner here than on the tundra below.

Once I followed a narrow gully of loose boulders and gravel stretches right down to the sea and found the little light blue sea lungwort, *Mertensia maritima,* the first blue flowers in all the abundance of rose and magenta, yellow and whites. Great mats of a plant with light green succulent leaves and tiny chickweedlike flowers spread across the gravel, the Honckenya described by Dr. Carey, chief botanist of our party. Flowers of the saxifrages and chickweeds grew abundantly even in rocky cracks where there seemed to be no soil.

It's magical the way these tiny, apparently utterly dead, plants retain the germ of existence through all the black icy months of arctic winter, and then come to life again so suddenly in a radiance of blossoming after a mere day or two, because they are touched by sunshine and warmth. It's the great abundance of light when it does come, so plant specialists say — light from the sky, reflections from rocks and water, snow and ice, plus unlimited supplies of moisture, rather than actual soil content which makes possible plant life as far even as the Polar Regions.

I stretched out on a low cliff just over the sea. A shallow rock trough lined with Vacciniums, crowberries, and mosses, made a wonderful scented, springy bed,

heated by sun, cooled by salt breezes. Once you know
your environment a little and have learned a few dodges,
you can be just as at home and relaxed in a tundra
world as in a New England garden.

Groups of white ice cakes, incongruous in the summer
blue and green of the sea, floated by, graceful things,
saluting each other with metallic clashes and tinkles.
Some were fantastic shapes like fairy castles. One was
as big as a small house; there was a pure white, upright
angel, then a gigantic pelican with great outstretched
wings.

White whales, with young gray ones (some people
say mature ones are occasionally gray also), dived in
and out, puffing and blowing with that delicious soothing sound as they fed placidly. Funny to watch them
standing straight up on their tails or heads, which remind one somehow of a sheep's.

Way out where wind struck the water, were purple
and emerald patches. And in the far distance, most
wonderful of all, great mirages like big white cliffs, so
shimmered and quivered and see-sawed that it made
you dizzy to look at them.

It was strange and restful to gaze upon that great sea,
which seems never to bear a man-made ship or boat
of any kind, and is always so utterly empty of human
signs.

Long black strings of American and white-winged scoters, those northern sea ducks with striking dense black and white plumage and red bills, floated on the waves, or flew up to change positions. Through the glasses I counted two hundred and ten in a single flock. Gulls, herring and Bonapartes, white wings lit by intense golden sunlight, flew low overhead, and terns fished off shore. A jaeger appeared (perhaps one of my pet family), and when a tern flew up with a fish, like a streak of lightning, the big bird darted at it, harried it ferociously, grabbed the fish that dropped from its very mouth, and shot off while the tern screeched with rage. This happened time and again. You could see where the name "parasite" comes from and why the jaeger is something of a terror to small tundra birds which it is said also to capture.

On the slow walk home — Terry had told me it was some two or three miles to a point not far from my tent — I followed close along shore wherever possible. Occasional small stretches of smooth sand and gravel were almost devoid of the usual sea life we're so accustomed to along Atlantic coasts. No barnacles, anemones, sponges or sea urchins; only a few starfish; very little sea weed and scattered forms of kelp.

But in tide-water pools in the rocks were hundreds of capelins — small six-to-eight inch, smeltlike fish —

dark olive with golden flecks above, sides of bright silver shading into lavender and pink with brilliant rainbow sheens. As exquisite as any tropical things. They're also delicious to eat; we've already had some collected by Terry and Luke. In fact all Churchill turns out to net and gather capelin from the shoreline and rock pools when the summer run is on. These fish are also said to form a big item in the whales' diet.

Higher up again in fresh water pools on the ledge, some form of tiny shrimp swam in countless numbers. Once I stopped and bathed in a flower-trimmed pool four-feet deep. The water, though very cold, was just bearable. It was the first complete bath I'd had since leaving home. Warm rocks and hot sun were blissful. But it was sheltered from the brisk breeze and in no time mosquitoes smelt me out again and I had to dress in violent haste.

At a point nearly opposite the Catholic mission where the environs of Churchill roughly begin, I left the ridge, and was surrounded immediately by about a dozen husky dogs and fuzzy bouncing pups. These huskies are something different from the pets of our civilized world. It really takes courage to face the huge and often fierce creatures. There are occasional gruesome tales of people being attacked by them. Only the other day one was shot for mangling a child. The dog was chained and was starving of course; and the child, with food in its hand, teased it.

It seemed to me the punishment should have fallen on the human system which contrives no better method of effective control of a fine animal than unceasing confinement and neglect. No matter how excusable an offense may be on the part of any of these dogs, there doesn't seem to be much forgiveness for them, slaves of men in this world. Someone said to me, "How would you have felt if it had been your child?" Incidentally the accident happened near a week end so the child was taken out by train for medical treatment at The Pas and, except for scars on an arm and leg, is expected to recover.

Many of the Churchill dogs are well fed and highly valued and therefore good tempered enough to be allowed to run free part of the time. There are many others, however, in particular those owned by Indians and breeds (but there are also some belonging to white men), who are in a sickening state; chained the entire season — some on perfectly bare flat rocks — without shelter from bitter storms, sun, and insects, starved, and utterly ignored. It makes you sick just to see some of them and I take long detours to avoid it whenever possible.

A miserable-looking white family, in a tiny shack not

far from Terence's, strike and kick their dogs at the least opportunity. Only two days ago I saw the children using a board to beat a starved-looking bitch, heavy with unborn pups, when the dog was trying to crawl under a building. The parents stood looking indifferently on. Furious, I rushed in and called Terry's attention to it.

But he shook his head; it was a sin. Those good-for-nothings were always doing things like that, but you couldn't interfere. No one interferes much with another man's dogs. In the North it's "live and let live" about most everything.

Just plain neglecting dogs is the worst of all to Terry's mind (and mine). These dogs are tough all right. They can go for days, weeks even, without food, but they can't stand it without water, not in warm weather. . . . Why, one time he saw a dog over on the flats chained and he knew from the way it acted that it had to have water. He hunted the owner up and told him, and the guy was ugly about it. Later in the day Terry passed that way again and there was the dog dead — he just plain died of thirst. That was all the good that his talking did. . . . And "them creatures" chained all summer, sometimes they die when the flies get after them. "Shure, last summer six died over the river in the Indian camp in one day. The flies [this is an all-inclusive northern term meaning both flies and mosquitoes] got in their ears and eyes and down their throats and probably just suffocated 'em, or else they died from sheer loss of blood. Shure, the safest dogs are the ones fed and cared-for and petted a bit. Most of 'em could be let loose sometimes."

I said I had thought dogs in the North were so important, at least economically, that people *had* to take care of them. How anybody could be so utterly callous to anything that works for him and sticks by him and often gives its life for him as these dogs do, beats me —

"Ye'd be surprised, Rosy," said Terence. "Ye're young yet. Ye haven't seen the evil there is in some folks — and the hardness. And some of us, likely, get kind o' used to seein' a lot of dogs suffer. We don't think much about it, more shame to us. But ye must remember, too, that man in these parts often suffers the same as his dogs do and the dogs are away tougher and can stand it better. . . . Take the Eskimos now. They couldn't live without their dogs and they take care of 'em — mostly. Better than some o' these Indians by a long shot. But everyone's not like that. A lot of the people here — not all — but a lot of 'em I guess, don't treat 'em badly; and there's many here thinks the world of their dogs and keeps 'em in fine shape. Some of the best teams in the country ye'll find right here. Take Slim Jim now. He's got dandy dogs. Got a cabin up the river where he keeps 'em. Works over 'em all the time. Paints 'em up with tar when the flies come and keeps a smoke fire going —.

"Shure, the police could do something. They'll go after a man for beating his dogs for nothing (they *have* to be beaten plenty when they fight or they kill each other!), but they don't come down near enough on the lads that just plain neglect 'em. But, I've known Mounties that do. The kind that take care of everything. They're the grand fellows. Some of 'em come from fine families in the old country. Well educated and all that. They do their jobs as police — none better or tougher I can tell ye — but they do a lot more because they're grand chaps theirselves. People go to 'em about everything — morals and sickness and religion and dogs and all and they always help 'em. Better'n some of these priests and missionaries a lot o' times. And when they see something they don't think right (and they see it too), they do something. Take the law in their own hands and fix it up to fit — "

We've heard all sorts of things with regard to the Mounties. And we've met the one here, Corporal East-brook, on several occasions. You couldn't call him exactly "romantic" but he's most awfully nice and helpful. Like men in every profession, the Mounties as individuals doubtless vary enormously, but to bear the reputation they've acquired, and accomplish what they have, must indicate on the whole a remarkable company. Especially, I think, those stationed at the remote arctic posts who receive no aid at all from outside and who, often alone, are responsible for territories of thousands of miles.

This ability to cope completely independently with a situation and the force of character which results, is what the real Northerner possesses. It's what our pioneer forefathers must have possessed. But what of the men in our world today? Protected and backed by all the power of law and society, they're fairly successful scholars and politicians and businessmen. But if at times they had to deal with situations without any such protection mightn't they be far more important scholars and politicians and businessmen?

Confronted by a situation such as Terry was discussing the other day, what, for instance, would Horace or Father have done? One of these trappers found in his cabin one winter a man, half-crazed, shot through the shoulder, lying in a pool of blood, waving a gun about. Not just a Mountie, but any of these men like Terry or Eric or Ronnie, would, with the minimum of effort and emotion, have done just what the trapper did: caught the man's gun before it went off again, bound up his wounds, washed out the cabin, taken him into Churchill. While Horace or dear Father would probably have been sick, or been shot, or fainted, or all three! Bill, because he's had to deal with strange men in strange places, might, I think, have done all right. Perhaps almost as well as the trapper.

Six

SOMETIME, EARLY JULY. Lost my calendar. Dates up here seem inconsequent anyway. The other night — must have been around one A.M. for it was slightly dark — I woke up in a regular sweat of fright. Horrid, low-pitched voices sounded just outside the tent; there were hideous noises of something hard hitting something soft, punctuated by squeals and groans. Sounded just like the time Bill and I caught old Mike kicking Aunt Katherine's pig up on the farm. Then I realized it was human beings having an awful fight, and that the hoarse voice — vaguely familiar — belonged to Terry. My first thought was that Dutchy had been headed for the tent and that Terry was engaged in one of those fisticuffs we've vaguely heard about. (Dutchy, providentially, has been largely occupied lately with a job on the railroad.) Had Terry been to the weekly dance and imbibed too much?

No liquor is supposed to be publicly sold here and so far we've not seen any intoxication, but most people have their own supply gotten in from outside. Anyhow from Terry's thick and unnatural tones he obviously was out of control for some reason or other. Finally I screwed up courage to peer out a tear in the canvas, enlarged to a peephole, and there, sure enough, was a large dim figure *kicking* a dark lump on the ground. I suppose I've never seen a really serious fight before and it made me sick and rather clammy. Finally the big figure stopped kicking and pummeling and the lump straightened up on two legs (not dead anyway!) and began to stagger off — and everything receded in the distance. I piled duffels and bags and boxes and everything against the door and went back to bed and finally to sleep again. A tent sometimes does seem so open and unprotected. . . .

Next day I cornered Luke about it; he wouldn't admit to knowing a thing. Then, timidly, I asked Terry, who seemed quite his usual sunny self. Immediately he looked completely offish and said, disapprovingly, some lad from the dance was creating a "dishturrbance" (Terry gets particularly Irish when he's annoyed) and had to be booted out of the café. Obviously it's one of those things I'm not supposed to poke my nose into. Up here, Mrs. Taylor says, a fight now and again is nothing to be disturbed about!

Early this morning we went to the station to watch the departure of the weekly train and say a final farewell to Dr. Stevens and Mr. Clayton, whom we shall miss horribly. To think I was rather scared at the idea of working up here with Dr. Stevens this summer. Wonder if we'll be able after this to listen with proper awe and respect to those famous lectures? Doubtless because we now love him so dearly and feel tickled whenever we think of him, we'll be infinitely more impressed and fascinated than before.

Compared to the crowd that greets the arriving train, few people go to see it off, but our particular pals were all there. Mr. Clayton, strolling about in his carefree way, said, "We'll certainly miss you and your goings-on! Don't think Doc Carey's strong enough to handle you girls, but there're plenty of others to take over. . . ."

He said he sure hated to go but his insides wouldn't stand any more of this diet and he'd be dead if he stayed here longer.

"Whatever it's done to his insides it hasn't dimmed his outside any," said Sue as we watched him and Doc, faces like red suns, climb aboard and shout vigorous repartee at prominent Churchill citizens. "If you ask me, it's about time they both returned to a soberer existence. Well, for heaven's sake, look at Dr. Stevens —"

The last glimpse we had of our revered professor on the moving train, he was hurling showers of kisses and yelling, "Good-by mosquitoes!"

Dr. Carey is going to stay another month or so, which is nice for Sue and me, since in addition to being an expert on arctic plants he has also an excellent knowledge of the birds. I've been botanizing with him lately. I ought to be able to have some of my collection accurately labeled now, thanks to him. Traveling miles and miles every day over the tundra to collect all the different species of plants, taking them home, laying each one out before it dries in the plant press, and writing up notes on its habits is one hefty job. Keying it down later in botany books and identifying it correctly is another, even worse one which ordinarily has to be done by experts in the university.

But gosh! Poor Dr. C. is such a bore. Even when we're tramping about he keeps recounting mournful incidents of his past — largely family disputes and frustrated arguments with university authorities. Who's interested in that world of petty affairs in this world where things are vital and big and impersonal? If something would *only* ruffle him up and make him messy. He never wears anything shabby or dirty; he seems utterly out of place with these rugged people. I've never quite taken in before how much incessant good-grooming sort of erases character and individuality. Maybe an attractive or unusual personality is more striking by contrast with shabby clothes, while the smart, consistently correct costume draws attention away from it?

Even miles off on the tundra Sue says Dr. C. "looks exactly like a college campus." But "he's always so gentle and polite," *she* thinks he's sweet!

During botanizing excursions we've also spent time making observations on lemmings and their burrows. Lemmings, famous for those great, mysterious migratory movements, are members of the same group of rodents to which our meadow mice belong. But species here are the "True Lemmings" which live in the Arctic and Far North, and are separate from the lemming mice (Synaptomys and Phenacomys) of more temperate ranges which my university pals are always trying to collect in our part of the world. The collared lemming, incidentally, is the only species of mouse that changes color in winter, sometimes becoming light, platinum gray or pure white.

Although we've seen voles or meadow mice, occasional droppings of arctic hares, signs of weasels, and a few red squirrels back at timberline, the most common small mammal here this summer appears to be the collared lemming, *Dicrostonyx rubricatus richardsoni*. Small hummocks along the foot of the Rock Ridge by Hudson Bay, are all pockmarked with their little burrows, which on excavation reveal small, round, grassy nests and green droppings. The burrows often contain willow heads, bearberry leaves, mosses, and saxifrages which the lemmings evidently feed on.

They're terribly cute little animals like great fat meadow mice with long, fine, yellowish-brown fur and tiny stub tails. Their small ears are hidden in fur, but their little black shoe-button eyes twinkle at you from behind stones and low plants. If you keep very still they sit up and stare — funny squashy little figures with large front paws draped on fat chests.

Most of the young now seem to have left the nests, but we found one well-furred litter of six, not far from a least sandpiper's nest. In a moment of unusual levity, Dr. C. put one of the lemmings in the nest beside the sandpiper young. And blest if the parent bird didn't rush back and try to gather the baby lemming, rather bigger than he was, up under his breast and start to brood it!

The little bird was in a quiver of fright at our close proximity and the strange and horrible happenings in the nest, but no danger on earth would force him to neglect home duties.

In the North, lemming populations are a big factor, since lemmings are a very important food for certain animals — notably the arctic fox whose abundance is so vital to man in this part of the world. The presence or absence of this fox in any given region fluctuates

[111]

considerably according to the lemming population. Weasels and raptorial birds, like the snowy and short-eared owls and rough-legged hawks, also follow the lemming distribution. Lemming skin is used sometimes for trimmings; little Eskimo children, Terry tells us, make dolls' clothes — tiny parkas and trousers — out of the delicate, silky fur.

We used to read a story about the tremendous lemming migrations in Scandinavia. The way untold thousands of them leapt off cliffs of Norway into the sea. And how back in 1868 it once took a big steamer fifteen minutes to pass through a great company of the poor little creatures swimming and drowning in the Trondhjem Fjord.* Something — overcrowding, overpopulation, lack of food — seems to compel these little members of the rodent world, found so extensively throughout arctic and northern regions, to undergo periodic seasons of migration. In Scandinavia it may be a tremendous spectacular movement lasting off and on for years. In arctic North America, apparently it's smaller and less regular. Sometimes the lemmings move in big companies, sometimes smaller groups. But once they are started nothing on earth stops them till they die. They swim right through lakes and rivers — when they jump into the sea off Norway probably it seems

* Victor H. Cahalane, *Mammals of North America,* p. 502.

just like one more lake to them — and they go on always until they're drowned or snapped up for food by other animals. It is said that even caribou eat them on occasion. But even when a huge migration occurs enough lemmings are left behind, apparently, to start a new population.

Disease doubtless is another factor which also controls lemming numbers.

The lemming population in this part of Hudson Bay seems to run in four-year, sometimes three-year, cycles. This year at Churchill they are quite abundant again after being rare for a year or two. So they are on the upcycle.

I'm lucky that my work of collecting and photographing is out on the tundra all day, instead of skinning birds and blowing eggs in a smelly old shack. Dr. Stevens has left Sue a mountain of things to prepare — any number of egg sets and bird skins. But Sue's such an expert she dotes on it really. And next fall back at college everyone will be "oh-ing" and "ah-ing" at those exquisite bird skins, while no one will even notice the dozens and dozens of tundra plants collected and pressed by Miss Rosamund S. Reeve —

It was good to get a lot of mail from home recently, though obviously no one, not even Mother, has the faintest notion of what life is up here. I do hope that if

Bill or anyone else ever reads any of this aloud, adding choice comments, as has sometimes happened to certain epistles of mine in times past, he will *expurgate* with care.

Several beautifully expressed letters from Horace make me feel both homesick and irritated. Why doesn't he love more of the things I do? He does like the out-of-doors, from the viewpoint of picnics in choice, carefully selected spots. But his charming conversation becomes completely inept and tongue-tied the minute you begin to discuss the really vital aspects of life. I'm never quite sure whether he thinks it's not etiquette or just that he really has no formed ideas on such things.

Speaking of mail, in the café last night Slim Jim, his red, excessively thin countenance quite cool and comfortable (he *never* looks sweaty up here even in the most broiling sun), said he lost all his mail in the ice one spring — and then his girl too.

"What the heck you talkin' about, Jimmy?"

Said Jimmy, "Well, I was goin' up along that stretch o' sea ice just off Seal River some place and my sled went right through. *I* thought the ice was safe enough but we'd had some awful warm sun — Dogs pulled her out all right, but my load tipped right off an' six months o' mail went right to the bottom. Got it when I come in from the bush and was savin' it *all* up to read when I

got up the coast to Don's place — mail from the folks
and a whole pile o' letters from this girl down to Port
Arthur too — "

"Did you write and tell her 'bout it?"

"Shucks, what was the use? What'd she think o' me
losin' her mail like that? Packages in there from her
too. Things she'd made me, I wouldn't wonder — and
she thought the way I live up here is just wonderful
and awful romantic — !"

"Who was she, Slim?"

"Shucks, I've forgot now. Awful queer name — like
that liquor ad — what was it now?"

"Grant's, Jameson, Heidsieck, Paddy, Gordon's,
Booth's, Vat, Cointreau, Drambuie — ?"

"That was it! Drambuie. Betty Drambuie she was."

I've had several evening visits with Eric Grey in
the tent or out along the rocks. Up here you somehow
get to know people surprisingly well in a surprisingly
short time. There's something about Mr. Grey's mere
presence, even when he says and does nothing, that
makes one conscious of him the minute he appears anywhere, even among all these other strong and striking
figures. Each time we've talked he's so fascinating I
want to go on for hours, and because of this probably
terminate our conversations far more abruptly than I
would with another interesting male. And when this

happens there's always that gleam in those very deep, penetrating hazel (sometimes red-brown) eyes of his which makes your cheeks hot long afterward. That man doesn't miss a thing! Wonder if we're especially congenial, or is it because he talks of the big things and real things that so enthrall me? If there've been tragic elements in his past (and his age, probably mid-thirties, his hard mouth, and the sharp lines in that rugged face all indicate depths of experience), I think he keeps them there and, unlike poor Dr. C., never obtrudes them on the present.

Wonder if he's conscious of me as a female, or just interested, rather impersonally, like so many of these northern men, about what such a delicate creature can possibly have inside? Or is he just helping to pass idle hours with someone rather new to his ken?

I never can talk much to Sue about this sort of thing. She's just too forthright somehow, too filled with plain common sense. Dearly as I love her, I wish occasionally she had a little more romance in her. Men always love Sue. She's such a jolly, sturdy, soothingly-sensible little figure, but I don't think she or they often wax really sentimental over anything. Ronnie McIntyre with his delightful easy manner (I'm never quite certain whether I like those eyes of his — they're a solid sea-green blue, hard without depth like a tiny baby's) is on especially excellent terms with Sue. Far easier than Mr. Grey and myself, for instance! It would be nice for once to be that way with an attractive man. (Perhaps this is what happens if he becomes a husband?!)

I've also learned a bit about Eric's interesting past. Though his father's was an old English family, his mother was Danish. Both parents died in an accident when he was young and much of his boyhood, except for holidays with Danish relatives in Scandinavia, was spent with an English uncle and in English schools; and later he had two years at Cambridge where he fore-gathered with Ronnie McIntyre fresh from Scotland. But life in a university was too confining to their adventurous souls and they left to try sheep ranching in Australia. They made "a bit" in that and in prospecting, but the North was in their blood and they returned to England and Scotland, working finally to Iceland and thence to arctic Canada.

"Sure, trapping's a great game" — though he doesn't propose to spend his life at it. This country, however, is what he wants. Never again will he have connections with big business and a place like his uncle's office. He tried, "But it was absolutely no go."

Several new dogs, prospective members of next winter's dog teams, have been added to Terry's and Luke's establishment. Two are mere roly-poly pups like thick fuzzy balls; one with black and white coloring, the other soft gray all over. They're absolutely irresistible. Sue and I just can't refrain from taking them to bed with us once in awhile. They come to my tent and whimper on stormy days. Who could keep them out? Terry says they will get soft and be "r-r-ruined for worrk. . . ."

But the dog who fascinates me most is Nero, the son of a wolf. Many of these dogs away back were wolf descendants. Even now, some people here claim that Eskimos very occasionally breed their huskies with wolves to keep up the stock. Others think there is no truth in this. Anyhow it apparently does actually happen that once in a while a wild wolf is caught and kept in captivity. This was said to be the case with Nero's mother, a young wolf bitch, taken at one of the posts farther north, who became tame enough to breed several times with the sled dogs.

Nero is a beautiful strong dog, gray with tan markings, as tall but less broad than some of these other dogs. His very expressive, wild, reddish eyes, are wonderful. Terry bought him from an Indian who was maltreating him and though he won't quite admit it, values him highly. The dog mostly runs free and has now, after being very wary and offish, made friends with me, coming out often from under the café to greet me and follow me to the tent.

Seven

∿∿∿∿∿∿∿∿∿∿∿∿∿∿∿∿∿∿∿∿∿∿∿

J ULY 10TH. It was decided recently that Sue and I should make observations on territory across the Churchill River. Terence would take us over with his eighteen-foot canoe and a borrowed outboard "that very evening" when the tide was right. We rushed about making preparations; in double-quick time, we got together food and equipment with the help of Mrs. Taylor, who loaned us a compact, battered set of cooking utensils and a billy can for tea which had gone thousands of miles through the Arctic, she said.

When she was a young girl Mrs. Taylor with her mother and father, a fur trader, traveled extensively through the Northwest Territories. Often they covered on foot and with dog team several hundred miles or more during late winter and early spring, staying at night in their own camps, with other traders, trappers, or missionaries as the case might be. We asked Mrs. Taylor about the Mackenzie River region where we'd heard she once lived. She told us a little, speaking quite casually of one winter there when, for two months, she was alone with her father, who was laid up with an ax cut in the leg which he nearly died of. They were completely isolated, way off the beaten track, in a one-room primitive cabin. No other human being came by, and she, a girl of fifteen, got firewood and hunted game: squirrels, birds, hares, "Just anything I could lay my hands on," to keep them alive. Once they went five days without food. But they "came out of it all right — "

Promptly at the appointed hour that evening we were all set to start over the river, but the engine was not to be had. The next evening the engine was on hand, but wind was dangerously high; the next when wind and tide and engine all appeared to be in accord, Terence had a job which he had "promised long ago."

We went through all the stages of every newcomer to the North: extreme irritation, the certainty that if it had been up to us we would have gone to work and done something effective, utter despair and final philosophical resignation.

Five days later, having given up the entire idea completely, we returned to the café one evening after an arduous day collecting and photographing to find Terence waiting outside.

"Ye're late," said he. "But we'll be off across the

river right now. The canoe and engine are two miles up, beyond the H. B. dock — "

"But," we cried, "we can't go now! We haven't got food or sleeping bags together, or *any*thing — "

"Don't need 'em, don't need 'em," with an impatient wave of the hand. "Ye can use Jimmy Kelly's winter shack over there. It's got bunks and blankets and food to last ye months. If ye want to go at all ye'll have to come right now — "

No, no time to hunt up Dr. Carey and see if he wished to go along. The tide would be right, the wind might get up again, he must fix something on the engine. If we wanted to go we must come right away.

Feeling completely helpless and terribly tired, we docilely followed him and reached finally a small beach beyond the pier where the H. B. schooner is in dry-dock. Eric and Ronald were there (they were going to help us across apparently), and various strange men from the Department House Building who invited us in for tea while we waited for Terence to deal with the engine. The Department House, part of a row of neat little offices and bunk houses, appears to be living quarters of all the head engineers and chief business men and, for Churchill, is almost luxurious. Since we'd eaten nothing all day except a tundra lunch, the inky black tea, enormous scones and jam were lifesavers. The room full of interesting (and interested) men, plus the attentions of Mr. Grey and Mr. McIntyre, were reviving, and we emerged feeling capable of coping with life once more.

Two small seaworthy Eskimo boats, forty footers equipped with single sails and small engines, had come into Churchill that day from points farther north. And one of the Churchill engineers who spoke Eskimo suggested we should go aboard with him and visit the huskies. (Husky appears to be a term synonymous with Eskimo and is, I think, quite apropos.) We acquiesced with pleasure since Terry seemed to be having trouble with the engine. Probably it would give out altogether, weather and tides change again, and we wouldn't go anyway — an outcome we now felt trained to accept with complete equanimity.

Aside from the few who happened to be in Churchill the day my train arrived, these were the first Eskimos we'd seen at close quarters. The young Eskimo men were ashore, but on the boats were several old men, one with long, stringy, droopy whiskers like a walrus, women, children and babies. The women wore voluminous long skirts and sweaters or parkas, sealskin boots, and bright plaid shawls draped over heads or shoulders.

They were simply charming. So jolly and friendly, unlike some of the rather somber Indians we've encountered thus far. Their round, plump, dusky cheeks were so deeply red, their squint eyes so sparkly, their black hair so shiny.

The engineer gave us plates of biscuits to pass around and the Eskimos laughed and laughed and repeated *"Mutna"* (thank you) again and again. We spent most of the time on board one of the boats labeled the *Now-yah* (meaning gull). A light-brown baby with a name which sounded like Alacoot, suspended in a blanket from its mother's shoulders, was pretty as a picture. The Eskimo tongue sounds soft and not unmusical — not guttural, as I supposed. They all seemed healthy and at ease, as if they completely accept life and people as they find them.

When we were about to go ashore again, five Eskimo men, young and middle-aged, all dressed in wool trousers, sweaters, and sealskin boots, came back to the docks. Their skin was very dark, their heavy, oily hair was worn in short bobs coming down over foreheads and ears like a black cap. Several had long straight noses, sharply-cut mouths, and prominent cheekbones which, with tilted eyes, gave them a Mongolian cast of countenance. One very short thickset man, pipe protruding from his mouth, had a really wonderful face — deeply-lined and crinkled and black, so keen, dignified, and expressive it engraved itself on your mind. They stood there on the dock, poised and self-possessed; just friendly and interested, not at all forward or inquisitive.

Finally Terence was actually ready and, with several false and spluttering starts on the part of the engine, we were underway at last beneath flocks of wild ducks, old-squaws and mergansers, and sea gulls black against the sunset sky, out through rose-tinted waters and white whales.

Eric Grey sat facing me in the canoe. It struck me suddenly that he is much too masterfully apt to take entire charge of me. I seldom get a chance to talk to Ronnie whom I certainly like equally well — better probably! So, abruptly and most ungracefully (exactly in that manner I deplore in our dear Puritan relatives), I turned completely away and began to talk exclusively to Ronald who sat behind. Mr. Grey certainly can take a hint, for during the rest of that evening, and the entire trip for that matter, he ignored me utterly.

Soon after ten we reached the Chipewyan Indian camp on the wild and little-frequented opposite shore. There were no trees — only flat bleak tundra stretching endlessly away, and low black rock ledges along the river. You never saw such a sight. Some dozens of old, patched canvas tents and caribou-hide tepees and campfires surrounded by dusky figures, were silhouetted against a deep orange sky. The air was spicy with smells from spruce wood that was burning.

Since there were no trees to fasten ropes to, and stakes can't be driven securely in ground full of solid ice, each tent had its ridgepole tied to a tripod of poles at either end. The ridgepoles, extending some feet out in front to a third tripod of poles, were used as racks for clothes and quantities of drying fish, split and hung by the tails. Everything — food, clothes, moccasins, dog harness — was hung on poles out of reach of the dogs. The side pieces of the tents, instead of fastened to ground pegs, were tied also to horizontal poles. Beside one tent was a tiny flat toboggan with high, caribou skin sides — just big enough for a baby or a big doll. Once a little Indian girl carelessly dropped in it a fuzzy puppy, which as carelessly bounced immediately out again.

A very old lady, a striking figure with a red scarf on her head (the Indian women and girls wore bandanas around their heads instead of shawls like the Eskimos), sat off by herself on a rock, a large motionless dog beside her. She looked out over the river, toward the old ruined fort way off in the distance and the sea beyond, and never moved a muscle during the entire half hour we were there. Another old lady seated on the ground, picked up a smoking cigarette butt thrown down by Ronnie and put it to her mouth. Blanket-wrapped papooses, strapped snugly to their little boards, were asleep everywhere; dark figures spoke low together around the fires; young boys were silently pitching coins.

The whole scene was quiet, like the quiet, big earth and the evening around them. No single voice or noise seemed to stand out above another, and the arctic twilight colors glowed and glowed and painted the water of river and sea. A new moon off to one side was perched exactly on top of a low rock cliff. It all looked quite unbelievable.

Terence and Ronald and Eric talked softly with Indian men whom they seemed to know. The presence of our party appeared to create no distraction, no particular disturbance, or curiosity.

When at last we reached the dwelling house of the old, original Hudson's Bay Post at Munck's Cove, some miles on up the river, we found the post manager away but "Old Mary," a Cree Indian of great antiquity, greeted us with a warm and toothless smile.

"And how are ye, Mary darlin'?" cried Terence as we all marched in as if we owned the place. (Nobody up here thinks it at all odd if you walk in a house demanding tea and food at any hour of the day or night.) "Shure it does my heart good to see ye again. Good lookin' as ever ye are — "

"Go on, Terry, Mary's my sweetheart," said Ronnie,

beaming charmingly upon her. "Those meals she's given
me when I've stopped by dead beat in winter. . . . And
we're all starved now, Mary. These young ladies haven't
had a bite to eat all day. . . ."

"Tea'll do, Mary dear," said Eric, "and some of those
tea cakes of yours — what, you haven't got any when
you knew I might be coming? Bread and jam then'll
do — "

Amid shouting of orders, shoving and pushing, and
delighted hoarse chuckles on Old Mary's part, she and
a young Indian girl hastened to comply. Her gaunt
bent figure moved lightly and easily about the big
old kitchen with its low, smoky ceiling. Her thick iron-
gray hair was drawn back smoothly in a knot, her
brown-yellow face (what a face) was wrinkled in a
hundred creases, like the shell of a walnut, her black
eyes were as bright and quick as a bird's. She looked
ageless, as if she really couldn't die. It gave you a
creepy feeling. . . .

"No one knows how old she is," Terry told us. "Over
a hundred maybe. Some of the oldest people in Churchill remember her a grown woman around this country
when they were young yet."

We were grateful for more tea. I'm really getting to
be a full-fledged northerner; I can down tea now every
few hours without the slightest difficulty. After this,

I'll never be able to enjoy the pale dishwater one gets at home.

Fascinated, we looked around at those great, thick, white-washed walls and the windows set way back in them. It was really a good-sized house; it looked as ageless as Old Mary herself. There was a big plain table in a sort of dining room opening off the kitchen, bookcases full of old classics — Scott, Mrs. Humphrey Ward, Thackery — with occasional oddly modern trash scattered through them, and a low ceiling lit by a lamp with flaring white mantle. Although still partial daylight outside, the small windows let in little light.

Sue and I had begun to wonder where we were supposed to sleep anyway? Or maybe not at all. They all behaved as if it were the middle of a day instead of the middle of a night. Finally after we'd all sat round for an hour or two, looking at books, playing cards, having a second round of tea and biscuits proffered by Old Mary, I reminded Terry that Sue and I had a long day of work ahead; we'd like to get some sleep; could he show us that shack now — ?

He seemed surprised at this (must have taken it for granted that we'd stay up all night), but "shure" he'd show us right now, and after a bit the rest of them'd be on their way, too, back over the river.

Kelly's shack was about a mile off in a sheltered spot

near the low granite ridge that stretches north and east
back of the post. In the orange-red twilight, with dawn
so near at hand, everything looked dimmed and weird
and oddly displaced. As we approached the tiny shack,
a large, gaunt, ghostly dog figure vanished behind a
small shed. "Some poor creature from the Indian
camp," remarked Terry indifferently. I went round the
shed to look and call it softly. And there, peering out
underneath, were two wild, terrified, anxious eyes and
a cowering form, pitifully thin and ragged. I took a
pilot biscuit out of my knapsack, but at my first motion
the animal backed up under the shed and disappeared.

Terry produced a key from some mysterious spot
around the woodpile and we went in. The inside of the
tiny fifteen by twelve foot shack made of boards and
gray logs, as seen by the light of a small oil lamp, had
stout double walls, a small double glass window, two
narrow wooden bunks, an iron stove, some two and a
half feet in length by one foot wide, shelves stacked
with old supplies — flour, corn meal, sugar, powdered
milk, tea, a partly used gigantic can of very ancient
marmalade, a half-full can of aged lard. Tin plates and
cups, eating utensils, some clean, some soiled, were
stacked in a dry basin as though they'd been left there
hurriedly the previous winter. There were partly-used
bottles of whisky and rum.

Jimmy Kelly had gone outside for a month or two. Shure, it was all right for us to use his shack and anything in it. Any friend of his (Terry's) was a friend of Jimmy Kelly. Many a man, especially in winter, had been glad for Jimmy Kelly's place. Terence pointed out we could stay there "comfortably" for weeks if necessary, said he would return late the following evening unless it came up a blow, and departed cheerfully.

We were suddenly just too exhausted to be concerned about anything — our complete aloneness in such strange surroundings, the harshness and odor of the blankets which made us long for our own sleeping bags. We didn't wake till a brilliant morning was well advanced, and then we lay looking with greatest interest at the tiny room, picturing the hardened men who stay there, coming in from the months of utter isolation and bitter cold of their trap lines, to this, a haven of comfort and luxury. Sleeping on these same blankets and pillows, gray and greasy from endless usage (we used our rolled-up jackets). A few pictures and old calendars were tacked to the walls.

"*There's* what you keep seeing in at least half these shacks and what makes these people so extra interesting to talk to," Sue said as we looked at books on a shelf above her bunk — a Bible, an English dictionary, a medical book, Wells's *Outline of History,* a dozen old novels, Dickens and Conan Doyle, some Canadian and American authors. There were aged magazines — *True Story, Movie, National Geographic, Saturday Evening Post*, and, believe it or not, a five-months-old *Atlantic Monthly*.

Here's the way a man reads a book up here — I've heard the men in the café on the subject: Perhaps he's alone and storm-bound in a camp for days. He has one book with him and he reads it from cover to cover, for there is nothing else to do. Then he goes back and reads it again, going over and over parts he especially liked or parts he didn't understand or disagreed with. He goes over those bits with a fine-tooth comb digesting them in his mind and talking out loud maybe. A man alone often talks out loud.

He reads with surprise and usually amusement, the endless pages or chapters of detail about one small adventure. And he thinks, "My God, if I were to write at that rate, of things that happened to me, it'd fill fifty books instead of one!"

Apparently most of these men, even when they have partners, prefer to live alone in winter and meet others only occasionally. Must be some job, cooped up for weeks on end in a place like that shack, for instance, to get on with another person, however congenial.

At Terry's the other night the men were discussing the distance they go in winter to get a book. No one appeared to think traveling alone fifty or a hundred miles on foot — it's so rough one seldom rides on a sled but runs along behind — for the loan of a single book was anything out of the ordinary. They talked of someone called Harry (Ronnie and Eric said he'd been a friend of theirs) taking a forty-mile trek last winter to his partner's cabin to get a volume on English history (of all things). He went through the ice of some river up there on the Barrens. His dogs must have dragged the empty sled to safety and then, finding no trace of their master, continued on along the trail fifteen miles to the other man's shack. When he saw Harry's empty sled and backtracked all the way to the river, he found Harry's footprints leading up to a hole in the ice. Harry's body was never found. . . .

After hefty struggles with the stove and leathery pancakes, bitter marmalade and tea, Sue and I went out into the morning, as softly sweet and blue as a May day at home. As we looked back across the great river, unruffled by winds or any signs of humanity, blue and silver under piled cloud masses, we saw an exalting and a thrilling sight. A big flock of whistling swans, a hundred or more, flew silently upshore — a great white mass of bodies, wheeling this way and that, catching light and shadow like a huge silver curtain swaying in a breeze.*

Near the shack was a small cutout slash in a gravel bank. And there, sure enough, beneath eighteen inches of roots and gravel, was a three-foot layer of ice. Until we actually saw this I don't know whether we'd really believed in the "solid ice just below the surface" idea — I went to see if my dog was still behind the shed, hoping it might have gone. But when I knelt down, there underneath were the two, terrified, questioning eyes again. And the minute I spoke they vanished as before. I left two breakfast pancakes and a pilot biscuit, because the ones put there the night before had disappeared. Sue, tolerantly sympathetic, pointed out it would do no good — only make the dog more unhappy when we'd gone. Very sensible, Sue always is.

Then we headed for a flat sweep of tundra and muskeg, which stretches from the river on one side, across for some miles to low rock ridges and lines of small

* Mrs. Angus MacIver, who lives with her husband on a tributary creek twenty-five miles up the Churchill River during the trapping season, told the author of the great flocks of swans which they see from their cabin on the river during spring and fall. As the swans, in their thousands, are continually rising and flying, and alighting and rising again, they talk to each other with lovely bugling notes; and the view of them as they cross the water reminds her always of sheets flapping in the wind on a beautiful, warm summer's day. So strong is this illusion that, even on chilly spring and autumn northern days, this sight of the swans makes her feel warm and languid.

trees along the sea on north and east. It took an hour to get across to the broad plateau, extending north several miles along the coast from the point where the old fort lies by the river mouth, to a great tidal basin called Button Bay. The ground was exceedingly swampy and interlaced with winding ponds which had to be skirted.

There were the wonderful, surprising, wine-red pools again connected by clear, little streams of golden water running over pebbly bottoms. It was a marvel why they even run at all in such a flat place. A species of small frog, like our New England pickerel frog, was around the pools. This was the first amphibian I've observed up here, but the others have seen a few wood frogs in timber, south of Churchill.

Flowers were far less numerous than on the Churchill side, perhaps because there was more muskeg, or perhaps because it was colder and the season less advanced. Huge snowbanks twenty feet thick were still piled in places along the low ridge. Birds, though abundant, were less varied as to species. Smith's longspurs rather than Lapland were common, and there were the usual numerous, sweetly plaintive white-crowned sparrows, sandpipers, snipe, phalaropes, and curlews. Old-squaws with their comical, yet somehow hauntingly charming cries, without which no tundra is complete, flew, as usual, distractedly off the ponds, only to alight as

quickly down on them again. We were surprised to
see a small flock of the little black and white snow
buntings, called "snowflakes" sometimes; when they fly
they look all white and stream through the air like a
miniature snow cloud. They are thought to be one of
the more strictly arctic forms that nests as far north as
land is to be found.

As we stood looking at a snowdrift on the ridge 200
yards away, we spotted through our glasses what appeared to be a huge husky dog, probably wandered,
we thought, from the Indian camp by the river. He was
a magnificent creature, very light gray, with wonder-
fully poised head and powerful hind quarters, in far
better condition and even bigger than any of the great
dogs we've yet seen. Three times he turned his head in
our direction, but continued to travel leisurely and
arrogantly along the ridge, never pausing or varying a
slow and remarkably graceful lope until he vanished in
a line of trees. Our presence disturbed him not at all
— he was a king.

"I bet that's a wolf!" I cried, grabbing Sue so suddenly she almost jumped out of her skin. "That's no
dog! It's too big! It doesn't act like one. It's an arctic
wolf I tell you — "

Sue was also instantly convinced, but her cautious
nature refused to admit this until we could describe it

to Terence and the others. It made us comprehend suddenly how wild and lonely this region was, remember that we were farther away even than usual from any protecting friends. But it made everything all the more thrilling. The North American wolf doesn't attack man except under extreme provocation. We felt in fact, far less alarmed at the idea of wolves than some of those tough-looking Indians, for instance. . . .

As we climbed the small ridge through fringes of stunted spruce, the character of the bird life changed abruptly and startlingly. One merely stepped from a tundra world to a timber world. Instead of the arctic and subarctic birds, we were surrounded by bells innumerable, brief and lovely liquid notes, of woodland gray-cheeked thrushes, the two clear, single, sweet, sad whistles of Harris's sparrows, the insectlike "tsee, tsee, tsee, tsee's" of black-poll warblers.

On the summit about 125 feet above the sea, was a broad plateau covered with little lakes, stretches of turf, and great masses of tumbled rocky outcrops. Away to north and east stretched the glorious sight of Hudson Bay, a brilliant cobalt, white ice fields shining and glittering. Ice was piled high along the narrow point where the old fort ruins lay, hazy and dim in the distance, and at other points all along the shore. Sea wind, strong and cold, blew off mosquitoes and black flies which had just begun to get unbearable down below. As we traveled north along the height, there was not a sign of man. Even Churchill's hideous grain elevator which, to our infinite disgust and the vast comfort of lonely travelers of the Barren stretches, shows in this flat, clear land for such surprising distances, had vanished completely.

Looking down finally over the gray and purple, brown and gold-green lichens and mosses which cushioned the rocky hollows, through a fringe of sharply pointed little spruce, etched blackly and delicately against the sea, lay Button Bay. Larger by far than we had dreamed, it stretched in a great half-moon indentation. Only one small part of its opposite shores could be distinguished through the glasses. Desolate and wild, utterly untouched, it reached straightaway to join the great seas coming down from the Arctic. The tide, partly low, gave some impression of the immensity of boulder-strewn mud flats stretching out from shore for miles. You could comprehend the difficulties, concerning which one hears so much, of landing anywhere along this shore of Hudson Bay. The sight of the deep harbor of the Churchill River mouth with its low, rocky headlands must have been a Godsend to mariners.

Masses of gray and inky clouds had begun to cover the blue of sky and sea, and little silver sheets of rain, alternating with shafts of brilliant light, obscured the other side of Button Bay and any land beyond, or lighted into dazzling whiteness, great ice floes on black waters.

Crouched in a mossy crevice of rock to eat pilot biscuit spread with the aged marmalade from Kelly's shack, we were awed and utterly silenced at the vastness of the wild desolation before us; its perfect beauty, bathed one moment in steel gray of angry skies and flaws of rain, the next in dazzling color from the bars of shining light.

There was a strange and awesome crashing of great ice cakes blown by strong winds against the shore below, with tinkles from a thrush and plaintive whistles of the Harris's sparrows, like a melody thrown against a backdrop of some weird symphony.

"Rosy, look, look, for Pete's sake — !"

A hundred feet directly in front of us, silhouetted against that spectacular sky and wild water, passed at a gentle trot a Barren Ground caribou. We could hardly credit our luck at this first sight of the arctic caribou, close relative of the Lapland reindeer. But there he was, a big shaggy beast, long fur of pale gray-tan spread over back and shoulders like a tattered mantle, bearing on his high-held head small trees — those great, beautiful, long, slender antlers with a black shaggy covering, extending by graceful curves into the broad, uneven palmations characteristic of the caribou tribe.

Twice he paused slightly, to sniff with great, black, wet twitching nose, the air in front. But unconscious apparently of our presence, for wind was blowing sharply from the sea behind him, he never turned toward us. Except for the slightest click of his feet (said to be made by loose cartilage in the ankles), he made not a sound as he trotted gently over the mosses and rocks on those great, cleft, padded hoofs, each some four by seven inches, said to supply one square inch support for every two pounds or so of weight (the average caribou weighs about 275 pounds), which will bear him up on the hard drifts of winter, across the oozy mud flats of summer. And he passed from view like a graceful slow-motion picture.

From the spread of his antlers, which looked to be over three feet (this spread is said occasionally to be as great as four), we judged him a male, for the female — the only American deer that wears antlers — has a smaller spread and less prominent brow tines. Though his coat is shabby now before he acquires the smooth brown summer one, still it was marvelous, and you could picture the gorgeous one of winter with its great white neck ruff extending back over shoulders and flanks. In "Si" Hobson's and the H.B.C. store, we've examined

parkas and sleeping bags made by Eskimos from the
caribou hide which keeps them as well as caribou warm
in the 60° or 80° below temperatures up here.

Observers say that caribou are splendid swimmers
and appear to have an extra buoyancy when they travel
through water. This may be due to the amount of fat
stored and the size of the antlers, as well as the fact
that the thick new pelage of late summer may trap
some air.*

On the pebble-and-boulder-strewn beach down below, we photographed ice cakes as big as small buildings, which had been piled on shore by wind and
waves. These must have come straight from the sea,
for they were pure white and not befouled with mud
and gravel like those left in shallow water. They were
like a giant's jewels, crusted outside with diamonds,
their hearts of purest aquamarine, so lovely and mys-

* The coat of a caribou is very thick and relatively long for a deer.
In the summer pelage, hairs are depressed and lie parallel to the hide,
but after the annual moult in July, during fall and winter, the hairs
grow in length and diameter. As a result of this continued growth,
hairs of the winter coat stand erect and form an exceedingly dense,
long pelage which provides excellent insulation. Caribou hair sometimes has been thought to be hollow. Careful examination of a hair
has shown that it has a solid cortex filled with large spongy cells like
those of other deer. (This information on the coat of a caribou was
kindly supplied to the author, November 1951, by A. W. Frank Ban-
field, chief mammalogist, Canadian Wildlife Service, who has been in
charge recently of a continent-wide caribou investigation.)

terious that one could lose oneself in another world inside them. The noise of their melting on the rocks, the great grinding and crunching of other huge pieces floating by, made a weird and desolate sound — the sound of the Arctic, untamed and free, beautiful and heartless.

Flocks of those large, heavy northern sea ducks, the famous eiders, something else we'd never seen before, were swimming in open water by the dozens or sitting on floating ice cakes. We counted twenty-three, both male and female, crowded tight upon one small ice pan. Some were squatted down with big, orange bills dropped close upon their breasts like fat old men with double chins. The females were an inconspicuous brown, heavily barred. But the males were just plain gorgeous. They had breasts and backs of pure white, white heads with dark irridescent crowns. A light vivid green, like ice where sun shines through it, bordered the crowns, back of head, and upper neck. White of the breast shaded into saffron yellow where the velvet black belly began. Their distinctive heavy orange bills extended up on the funny flattened feathered foreheads like two prongs of a fork, their heavy feet and legs were yellow-green. Occasionally males or females made passes at each other, rising up and flapping their wings, but for the most part they rested or fed lazily.

This was the common eider, the species most usual

here, but the king eider is also found. Eider nesting grounds are common in various localities along this coast.

Eric has told us how rigidly protected and encouraged the eider is through Scandinavia and Iceland for the value of its eggs as well as wonderful down feathers. Although supposedly protected here, how much law-enforcing can be done? In this great land who, except the Mountie responsible for a thousand miles perhaps, can tell when any species is being preyed upon exten-sively? Canada is so young, especially on her frontiers. Like the sad history of our own states there will appear to be unlimited supplies of everything till it's too late, and then with infinite labor and expense maybe she will try, as we've done, to bring back again some of her wonderful resources and wildlife.

Strange how shortsighted men are, as well as selfish. What foundation is there for thinking that the entire earth is man's to use or abuse exactly as he may choose?

A sudden rain squall drove us to shelter under tall rocks and just as the worst of it had pelted by, ten wild geese whose melodious honking had echoed far out in the bay, flew low just overhead, and one goose ducked down below the rest and saluted us with a single deep and thrilling trumpet note. Three arctic loons swim-ming offshore gave voice with the ghostly calls I deeply

love and have learned to expect as another part of the
harmony of a wild northern scene.

Sun came out again, hot and bright, and a thousand
tinkly rills descended from the ice chunks. The afternoon was well advanced when we climbed back over a
low, open rise known as Seahorse Gully. By the time
we struck back up on to the plateau again, we were
so hot (after recently having been chilled to the bone),
we took a bath in one of the dozens of clear small ponds.
The water was deep enough to swim in but so cold
that we spent more time sun-bathing on the warm
prickly lichens, silhouetted against the ice fields of
Hudson Bay. It was a marvelous spot for baths à la
nature. A stiff breeze drove off mosquitoes, the sun
was hot enough to keep us reasonably warm. Best of
all was the firm conviction that all other human beings
were miles and miles away. We dressed finally and
started back leisurely, intending to keep as far as possible to the better walking of the plateau until we must
leave it to cross the muskeg back to the river.

We rounded a slight rise and there, sitting like a
statue on a rock, a large gun over one knee, was a live
Indian.

Caring not at all for his unpleasant face and very un-
kempt appearance, we walked nonchalantly by and
greeted him politely. We then proceeded slowly along

the vague outlines of what looked like a game trail, but when we glanced back there was the Indian following a little distance behind.

"Only man is vile," said Sue bitterly. "Always trust a man to turn up and spoil things — you can't get away from them anywhere."

"Probably he's all right and this just happens to be his way too," said I without conviction. "When we pass through that bunch of trees ahead, perhaps we could cut down to the flats and shake him — "

We tried not to quicken our pace until we reached the shelter of the spruce. Then after an abrupt right-angle turn we tore breathlessly down steep banks, keeping always in the trees.

There was a flash of red and yellow just ahead and we jumped as if we'd been shot — It appeared again: a huge red fox, its fur the brightest and most lusciously thick of any I've ever seen. And then, a hundred feet ahead on a big thrown-up heap of earth beside a hole in the bank, we came on three fox cubs, the size of large cats, playing and somersaulting with one another. They saw us on the instant and froze — darling, graceful heads, big prick ears, sparkling eyes, black pointed little noses, red fluff coats, huge, plumy, black-tipped tails.

"Oh just look at that," gasped Sue and at her first breath of whisper, one single streak of red vanished down the hole. Presently a tiny head appeared in the opening, only to disappear the instant we raised the cameras. The light meter showed the light to be still good enough for pictures. Crouched behind a boulder, wondering whether an Indian or a fox would appear first, we waited breathlessly.

No Indian appeared; neither did a fox, and we'd almost given up when, suddenly outlined against the clear sky above the den, came a fourth small cub obviously just returning. No, he was dark, tannish-gray; he didn't belong to this litter. But he did! For he made a sudden dive down into the hole only to pop up again instantly, like a jack-in-the-box, followed by a red one. Three more times he came up alone and went under. Then, having accustomed himself to the sight of us, he stayed out beside the hole and began to play, stopping often to gaze in our direction, head cocked first to one side, then the other. He was the most beautifully furred and exquisitely marked little creature you ever beheld. A dark, almost black, shape like a cross ran down his back; the rest of him was tan and gray, soft as velvet, thick as a cushion, with vivid black and buff and yellow markings around the head and legs.

We were certain he was that rare and beautiful animal, a "cross" fox — the name derived from the color pattern on the back, not from disposition or crossbreeding. In our part of the world red foxes are largely red, but in these parts there are often four distinct color phases of the red fox: red, black, silver, and cross.

The trek back across the tundra to the river took hours and was a grim test of endurance. The wind had died and, in the still warm evening air, black flies, much more prominent over there than mosquitoes, attacked us in furious hordes. They're far worse than mosquitoes, for they squeeze inside your clothes and sting poisonously.

Nearly smothered by head nets, loads of field equipment and heavy clothes, exhausted by our forty-eight hours of intense activity without adequate meals or sleep, we were really played out. But we reached Kelly's shack at last.

And there by the shed was my dog again. This time when I walked toward it, though it retreated a little, it didn't vanish but wagged a faintly drooping tail and looked straight at me with the saddest golden eyes. I gave it four of six remaining pilot biscuits and it turned and followed me. It fairly made me cry, thinking what would happen when I'd gone again, the first human being perhaps who'd ever been even decently kind. Right then I *hated* this country. The useless suffering that man causes his fellow creatures makes me sick and desolate.

Of course I considered seriously taking the dog home but everyone knows what happens so often to these arctic work dogs when they become pets in warm climates. And if I were to begin up here to try to buy every dog that makes me heartsick —

Back in the shack I stretched out on a bunk and joined Sue in eating the last of the hardtack. Our backs were masses of welts and our shirts a wet red, bloody mess where hundreds of black flies had been crushed inside. I didn't care whether Terence ever came or not, but when we finally heard an outboard chugging on the river, Sue, already recuperated (nothing ever gets that girl down), rushed out to look with the glasses.

Terry landed near the H. B. Post. Our pals were with him again and another strange man. Sue insisted we go over and meet them, though I didn't see why we shouldn't wait in the shack till they came for us.

This time Old Mary expected the post manager, so we would "wait a while," said Terence. Tea, strong enough to make your hair curl, and bread and butter which, though not the real meal we craved, were very reviving.

An hour passed full of the usual fascinating talk by the men. Mr. Grey was still not on speaking terms with me. The trapper, one Joe, who'd brought them over in his canoe, didn't appear. They were all interested in our description of the caribou and wolf and foxes. A wolf without doubt, they said, for wolves are seen often, especially in winter; sometimes on the very edge of Churchill.

"Maybe they don't attack man," said Terence, "but I'd hate to have to chance it! Some of the sights I've had of 'em when I've been on me own would make your hair stand up! One time I saw fifty-three on a lake in winter — counted 'em. They were in three or four bunches, sometimes all together. They weren't scared of me, I can tell ye, and the way them cold yellow eyes of the nearest ones — about 100 feet away — looked at me. . . . God! I was scared. They sure make way with the caribou too. Herd 'em up like dogs and then kill 'em. . . ."

"Sure they kill 'em," said Ronnie. "They have to for food, but they don't slaughter them in numbers like the white men do and then leave 'em to go to waste. Hundreds of years before man, just remember, wolves and deer lived together in healthy numbers. The thing that's exterminating the caribou is man himself."

Eric said (I'm quoting all this as accurately as possible for I thought it so very interesting):

"Wolves are strange creatures. Lord! but they must have wonderful brains. Remember that bitch last winter, Ron? Still makes me sick to think of it. . . .

"We were camped one night way up the coast, inland. Our dogs were tied up; we had a big fire and this wolf, dragging a shattered leg, came right up to us. Thin, so it made you sick to look at it. Thought at first it was mad, but it just stood there, looking at us. I tell you that wolf had a mind and soul. It *wanted* us to kill it. It came on purpose. We went to bed in the tent and left it standing there. I kept looking out and it stayed there, its eyes in the firelight looking at me. Couldn't stand it. . . . I got up and shot it —" *

Around midnight when it was dark inside those thick walls, Henry MacLeod, the post manager, arrived — a very young chap for such a responsible job, extremely good-looking with blond curly hair and a handsome sunburn. He was completely unperturbed to find, in his dining room in the middle of the night, a lot of people, two of whom were scientifically-minded young ladies from the states.

More tea and biscuits and then at last in that weird sort of light which always seems a strange combination of sunset and dawn, we wandered down to Joe's canoe left pulled up on shore. And there was no canoe.

"Jumping Judas," said Terence, who for once apparently had to be back in Churchill on time for some-

* This experience was recounted by John Stanwell-Fletcher.

thing. "That damned son of a bitch! He's left us!"

The H. B. boat was over on the other side of the river. There was nothing to do but to walk some distance alongshore to Denny's place and see if he could take us over. And more miles, after all that Sue and I'd already done, were a mere drop in the bucket.

Finally we came to a lonely, completely isolated low house, large for these parts, its surroundings and sheds rather neater and better kept than usual. Fine-looking husky dogs, who had gotten up to roar at our approach, were chained beside well-made kennels and several huge toboggan sleds, or *komatiks,* were laid on their sides nearby.

The men went in to pay respects to Denny and his household with whom they're all warm friends, for Denny many times has given them food and shelter and never refused help when they've been hard pressed. Sue and I, not knowing quite what was expected of us, said we'd wait outside, and Eric took us to a bench along the wall of a shed. Eric takes far more initiative than Ronnie and is considerably more sensitive than Terry, for instance. (Yet there are those times when Terry is plenty observant and I suspect him of a deep-seated prejudice against pampering us. Sue and I are "out for experiences." We can just take what's good for us or lump it!)

If Denny couldn't take us over, would we go inside and spend all night there, we wondered?

But after a time Terence appeared again with a wiry, small man, a most striking-looking individual with a lean dark countenance, small moustache, and black sparkling eyes, who regarded us with a flash of white teeth and such a twinkle no one could resist liking him.

Denny and Terence and Ronald pulled the canoe down a tiny beach to launch and we all climbed in. Ronnie said Eric was going to stay over and visit on this side for a while.

The still water was filled with white whales. Our canoe weaved about among them; they were so close that the men reached out often and whacked them with a paddle. The rosy dawn had begun. And, weirdest and most marvelous of all at that hour, was an aurora, waving arcs and streamers of green and throbbing light against the pink, morning sky. The colored arcs dissolved continually into quivering mists of light that shot suddenly over all the heavens, like swiftly moving cloud shadows across a landscape, and vanished again as quickly. Imagine a thing like that across the great solid white, and vast frozen lands, of arctic winter when "the lights sing," as people call it.

Although scientists don't entirely agree about all the marvelous phenomena of the aurora, Doc Carey says that electrically charged particles from the sun's surface are pulled toward the magnetic pole. At 100 or 200 miles altitude these strike electrons from the shells of oxygen and nitrogen atoms and so become luminous. The "singing," or tingling, sensation which so impresses some observers of the really miraculous auroras of the Far North, must be due to the electrified atmosphere and discharges close to the ground. For the lights themselves are too far off to be heard.

I kept thinking of what a world it is up here, of miracles and beauty, ugliness and hardness, strange atmospheres and people — It was an odd time and place to long for Horace and think of that gentle, clean, scholar's face of his, his unvarying consideration and steadiness. But I'm glad there are men like Horace.

Sue and I sat together facing stern and encountered the twinkling regard of Denny so often that we were tickled and a bit nervous. Then at last we all reached Churchill and disembarked with warm thanks. Here, one doesn't offer money for such trips. (Terry says he takes us on short trips any time for the "enorrmous" pleasure our company gives him!) Only on long excursions does one help pay for gas or use of an outboard for example. But some day Terry will do something especially nice for Denny in return.

Got to bed finally, alone in my tent at last, in broad daylight around 3:30 A.M. I never was more thankful to get anywhere. Felt simply done in, both physically and mentally.

Eight

ᵒᵒᵒᵒᵒᵒᵒᵒᵒᵒᵒᵒᵒᵒᵒᵒᵒᵒᵒᵒᵒᵒᵒᵒᵒᵒᵒᵒᵒᵒᵒ

J ULY 14TH. We've just had the most thrilling expedition to Fox Island.

The day after our trip over the river there was another howling storm. It's amazing the way bad weather out of a clear sky can blow up in a few hours. But I was more than grateful this time for a good reason to stay in bed. Didn't feel as though I *could* get up, or wanted to see anyone again, ever.

As for Churchill, no one would be up for half the day at least. When weather's good the whole settlement bursts into activity. Men work by the long evening until midnight, dredging the harbor, building shacks and boats and sleds and things, repairing winter damages, fixing up for summer. You can hear them pounding again at dawn; or else they never stop all night. Then a storm comes up and they sleep in all day. Stores aren't open. Terry and Luke are curled in sleeping bags on the café floor till noon. Except for the date

[154]

of the train arrival, one week day is just like another. It appears to be Indians chiefly who attend any church services.

Exactly like animals, humans here are in tune with the weather. This seems a sane way to behave, up in this land where man and his little activities are swallowed by natural forces, dependent so continually on nature's changes of season and mood.

Dr. Carey had been negotiating for days with one Tommy Roe, a young Eskimo born at sea in a tiny sailboat on Thomas Roe's Welcome, that big stretch of water between Southampton Island and the far northwest shore of Hudson Bay. For the quite modest sum of $25.00, covering gas and rent for an outboard for several days, Tommy Roe finally agreed to take us to Fox Island. Fox Island lies about twenty-five miles east of Churchill off this point of coastline which stretches some thirty miles northeast into Hudson Bay and culminates in Cape Churchill. So far the huge prices paid for guide service don't seem to apply to this part of the world. Anyhow after hefty struggles with the usual opposing barriers — weather, winds, tides, lack of engines, suitable helpers — that erect themselves the minute anyone wants to take a trip or accomplish something, Doc Carey's persistence won out. (Numerous firsthand encounters with tough northern elements have dimmed a little of that professorial primness.) And I think an interview with Sue's and my harmless sunburned countenances and our vast enthusiasm helped a good deal to persuade Tommy too.

The weather cleared shortly and just about everyone and everything seemed actually to be all set. But the very morning we were to start the man who knows that part of coast really well and was to have gone with us, didn't show up. It was discovered suddenly that he had gone on another trip somewhere. All this wasted another valuable day, but finally we got hold of Eric Grey, who is an excellent boatman. (He's been unusually affable since the visit over the river!)

Two mornings after the storm, we were all off at an early hour in Tommy Roe's big twenty-foot freighting canoe, more seaworthy than most, equipped with an eight horsepower outboard.

Each of us, typically well-trained travelers in remote places, had packed our gear with greatest care, and possessed rolls composed of sleeping bags, change of clothes, films, skinning kit, plant presses, all very neatly and compactly done up. It was, therefore, very entertaining to have Tommy Roe, a far more seasoned northern traveler than any of us, stroll up at the last minute and hurl casually into the canoe an odd assortment of articles: a tattered bedroll, a big knife, a heavy cup, a huge caribou skin, a thick china plate, a fork, a spoon, a loaf of bread, a pair of sealskin boots.

These sealskin boots are wonderful things — hand-sewn by the Eskimos, they're no heavier and not much bigger than a pair of socks; and they're completely waterproof and far easier to take along on a trip than rubber boots. Their disadvantage (I've experimented with a pair lent by Mrs. Taylor) is that they're frightfully slippery and don't provide much protection against sharp rocks and stones.

Tommy had been along that coast once before. His reputation for reliability and seamanship are A-1, and having been educated at a mission he speaks English freely. He is also a quite charming person, small and strong and round and dark, with an irresistible smile. When you know people like Tommy you can understand why mixed white and Eskimo marriages on occasion turn out so happily.

For a wonder the weather still held and everyone was in great spirits. Tommy Roe was seated stern by the engine, Eric with his heavy paddle in the bow, while Dr. Carey, Sue, and I were in the center on the caribou rug spread over food boxes and sleeping rolls.

In such a blue and radiant morning all the ominous warnings about getting to shore if wind changed before ice floes moved in on us, or waves became too high for

Tommy's canoe, getting caught miles from shore on mud flats, or taking food enough for weeks instead of days, seemed utterly farfetched. (Though an acquaintance of Doc Carey's last year who set out on a ten-mile three-day trip got stormbound up the coast and was gone three weeks!)

As we rounded the Merry Rocks and headed along the coast which turns gradually eastward toward the Cape, all signs of Churchill and humanity receded in the distance. White ice fields were faintly visible to the east, but a wind blowing off shore had pushed them far away. The Rock Ridge southeast of Churchill changed character gradually. First, it was high and bare, interspersed with its tiny beaches; farther on it was crowned with black lines of small spruce; then it dwindled and disappeared entirely in great sweeps of gravel and long beautiful sandy beaches that rose gently into dunes carpeted with dense green mats of plants like vivid grass, or blended into flat, flower-filled tundra reaching away into blue distance. Each beach was so lonely and wild and utterly untouched, you could hardly bear to pass by without landing at least to explore and savour it.

There was not a sign of another boat (there seldom is apparently except during the two months or six weeks of summer when the ice goes) or any other human thing on that whole expanse of sea and coast. Compared to the teeming seas of so many parts of this globe, comparatively few men sail these waters or set foot on these untouched shores.

Small groups of old-squaws and huge flocks of white-winged scoters flew up as we chugged along. There were a few white whales; and very often the shining, dripping baldhead and comical bristly whiskers of a seal appeared above a wave and vanished even as you looked at it.

Tommy and Eric shouted ardent comments back and forth on the lusciousness of seal liver and Eric took occasional shots. Touchingly beautiful, great big, liquid dark eyes set in the funny bullet heads watched him raise the rifle everytime and sank invariably on the split second the shot rang out. You never saw anything so perfectly timed. Tommy Roe roared with laughter and so did Eric.

Seals of this part of the world are the Earless or Hair Seals, rather than the Eared or Fur seals of Alaskan and Pacific waters. The two most common forms here are the ringed, *Phoca hispida,* the familiar *"Netcheck"* of the Eskimos, and the harbor or ranger seal, *Phoca vitulina.* A little farther north are other species like the harp seals and bearded seals. These funny warm-blooded mammals, so common in northern seas, so awkward on land, so marvelously graceful in water, their limbs turned into flippers, outer ears (much reduced or absent) as well as nostrils protected by valves, sleek slippery bodies densely furred, or, as in the seals here, covered with coarse hair, are highly valuable to man. In these parts seals are vitally important for their tough waterproof skin, which is used for clothes and all sorts of equipment; for oil which comes from dense layers of fat; and for their meat, an excellent food, especially for sled dogs.

I've never seen Mr. Grey so attractive. He was clad in an Eskimo tan parka of Hudson Bay blanket "loaned by a friend." (Up here, among friends at least, wearing apparel as much as houses and supplies appears to be common property.) With embroidered hood thrown back, which set off his big shoulders, Eric looked much younger — gay and boyish and carefree. Those astonishing eyes of his sparkled and the hard lines of his face and mouth were wiped away.

Anyhow who could be anything but gloriously happy on such a fresh and life-giving sea? Mosquitoes were nonexistent, sun brilliant, the water every shade of emerald and sapphire and amethyst. I never can get over the amazing color variation in Hudson Bay, due perhaps not only to variable lights, but to the vast shallows shading with deeper water — solid black, black-green, gray, silver, bright larkspur blue, pale blue, purple, lavender, pink, and gold.

Wonderful mirages — those fantastic, mysterious, enchanted things, so real and yet unreal — shimmered in the distance. Several were as high as small hills or cliffs. Two masses moved sometimes in opposite lines up and down like a giant see-saw. They make one feel as the aurora does: that here again is something beyond the ken of man; too great and imponderable for even his scientific knowledge to comprehend completely.

As usual we applied to Dr. C. — I make fun of him, but he's truly wonderful to have around! — a regular live encyclopedia of versatile information which he can put simply and clearly. We begin to see why he's something of a famous professor. Mirages, he said, are especially characteristic of polar regions but are such complicated phenomena they can be described accurately only in formidable mathematical terms. Arctic mirages are termed "superior mirages," while desert ones, due to hot air layers close to earth are "inferior mirages." The type of superior mirage here is due to warm layers above cold ones. But these are some distance above the surface and, because of this high altitude, the mirage here is not just a phantasy like the "lake" on a desert, but a sort of looking-glass in the sky reflecting a solid object — ice or land, etc. which

is usually within fifty miles, but greatly distorted sometimes by the curvature of light rays. Arctic mirages
have been responsible for all sorts of false reports of
nearby land masses, mountains, and so on which in
reality were very far off, or not in the position or area
described. On the other hand, these mirages may be
useful things since they indicate the definite presence
of some actual solid formation.

Toward noon we came in sight of a long narrow point
of land sticking straight out into the sea. On our side
it curved back around a big, shallow, basinlike cove,
and just along the water's edge I saw, through the
glasses, a small grove of dead sticks or trees. The grove
moved. It was made of horns. I cried "Caribou!" Instantly Tommy hushed the engine and Eric began
paddling us toward a rocky point to the left where we
might land without disturbing the herd. Dr. Carey
wanted movies, so he, Sue, and I crept cautiously out
from the low rocks and started very slowly along the
beach. The caribou at first were some four hundred
yards away. Apparently they saw us, for two bands
began to mill leisurely into one and we were able to
count sixty to seventy individuals.

Crouching behind isolated boulders or along the line
of low, grassy land that joined the beach, we got gradually nearer. When we kept still for a time the caribou

settled in a compact bunch, about half lying down right in the sea water (this was to escape the flies). As soon as we moved again, so did the caribou, walking some fifty yards in one direction; then whirling about in a solid phalanx exactly like well-drilled solders, all heads turned the same way (they practically kept step together), to walk fifty yards in the opposite direction. Each time a leader appeared at whichever end went forward.

It was a perfectly thrilling sight. Light shining through that giant mass of huge antlers made one think of a moving forest; or a herd of ostriches perhaps, the antlers like long and oddly-twisted necks. When they all walked in the shallow sea it made a great, swishing, splashing sound. A pair of rough-legged hawks, whose nest was on the low bare rock ledge, circled above us. Out on the cove, five arctic loons gave haunting, desperately lonely cries; and back on land, carried faintly by the breeze, were myriad songs and calls of curlew and plover and sandpiper and other shore birds. All the music of the tundra and wild and lonely places.

Some caribou with shorter racks were smaller than others. Although females, because they too have antlers, are hard to distinguish from young males, these were probably young bucks, Tommy Roe said. You could tell the older bucks which had huge racks sloping backward. At this time of year does are mostly farther north with the young fawns.

Even this size company of caribou, so tremendously exciting to us, made one realize what a herd of thousands must be like, moving during a spring migration from the winter grounds around timberline north to the summer grounds on the open Barrenlands. Or the incredible hundreds of thousands said to have traveled together in years past, which for days covered miles of land in a living mantle. So easy to stalk, that Indians and Eskimos depending on caribou for food and clothing, and finally the white man with his high-powered weapons, simply exterminated vast numbers. Now in many places the caribou have died out completely or are seriously depleted. The toll taken by wolves is nothing compared to that of man.

It is always the same wherever man appears in a rich and unspoiled land. Sad commentary on his "superior" morals and brains? More and more you become impressed, especially when you contact true wilderness areas, with the *stupidity* of man — his ignorance and lack of understanding and ridiculous inability to get on with other forms of life which were put here in this world just as surely as he was, and form such an essential part in the whole scheme of things. There doesn't seem to be anything particularly out of order in man's

[164]

using animals for food and clothing, especially in a wild land where he is dependent on them for his existence. All forms of life live on other forms. The crime lies in the fact that man has so needlessly exterminated whole races of animals, when he might have used carefully a limited supply: the wholly unnecessary and terrible suffering he causes, when he might just as easily (and for his own profit) have exercised careful handling and respect for their welfare; his utter lack of appreciation so often not only for their usefulness but for the very great beauty and pleasure and inspiration contributed by so many of them.

During the winter caribou bulls begin to wander away from the cows and by spring form separate bands. The animals feed on low shrubs — willows, blueberries, grasses and sedges — but their favorite diet of all, and what they live on most extensively during winter, are lichens, especially the reindeer moss. By the end of summer they have all acquired a heavy layer of fat, sometimes three-inches thick, Tommy told us. The bulls, with shiny new antlers, are ready then for the rutting season and heavy fighting matches. They are promiscuous but each keeps about a dozen cows in a sort of harem. Fawns, born in May or June, unlike many other young deer, are unspotted.

Slowly, for about a mile, we followed our herd of

sixty or more, and as slowly the herd receded from us, stopping now and again to browse a bit, when Dr. Carey with his Telephoto got movies at five hundred feet. Finally the caribou left the water and shore entirely and headed up a gentle slope. Inky black against the sapphire horizon, they were silhouetted for several minutes, then they vanished, a few antlers like the masts of moving ships, disappearing last.

We were off in the canoe again through the dazzling gold and blue of late afternoon, heading east in open sea, when Dr. Carey exclaimed at a strange white light on the horizon.

"Ice blink," said Eric. "Means ice fields over there. The kind that catch the ships. Sometimes only for a few days or hours if they're lucky enough to get on the edge where there's constant shifting. Sometimes they're caught and never get free. Many a ship's gone that way in the Arctic. If the boat's near shore, sometimes crew or passengers can travel over ice and get to land —"

The ice blink was a pale, yellow-white, low down in the soft distant blue. It seemed to quiver slightly, weirdly and menacingly, and made our day seem less warm and carefree.

Once we came to a group of small ice pans and Tommy climbed out on one and cut chunks to fill our billy cans in case there was no fresh water on Fox Island. When sea freezes, salt is lost slowly until the old ice is relatively free of salines; or if it comes from land and is made of snow or glaciers, it forms fresh water anyway. Here at least the ice of Hudson Bay seemed safe and manageable and familiar again.

But a little farther out were a few small icebergs. These, Tommy and Eric said, were forty or sixty feet high. They were something to steer clear of, for even a few tons breaking off made ten-foot high waves which would swamp our tiny boat. Through glasses, the bergs looked like little snow mountains with jagged peaks and valleys and precipices from which descended streams and waterfalls. Light brought out shades of gold and green, purple valleys, pink-lit mountain tops. Come down, perhaps, straight from the Arctic Sea, they looked quite enchantingly beautiful, yet threatening and merciless somehow.

Then we seemed to leave the neighborhood of ice altogether and went on through a summer sea. Our boat scared up flocks of common eiders, a small number of king eiders, more scoters and old-squaws; and once three swans, snow-white and lovely, flew very low overhead.

In the early evening, still so bright and warm it seemed like midafternoon, we came to Fox Island, a flat circular-appearing piece of land, about a mile long by three-quarters wide, at low tide connecting by a narrow strip of mud flat with the mainland. As we headed in to the pebbly beach we were astounded at a great yelping and barking like a puppy dog. There on the low, sandy, grassy bank appeared a small, gray, fluffy figure, the size of a cat, with black inquisitive face and tiny, rounded, pricked-up ears — a little arctic fox! All the time we were unloading he ran about and bounced and sat at safe distances watching these strange creatures, doubtless his first human beings, invading his undisputed world. (No one seems certain whether originally it was *Foxe* Island after the explorer of Foxe Channel fame, or *Fox* as it so appropriately is now after its own wild little inhabitants.)

There appeared to be at least four occupied arctic fox dens, and we kept seeing three other cubs as well as the first bold little one. All were smoky gray with tan markings and blackish heads, much smaller than our red fox cubs across the river. Tommy said they were probably some eight weeks old; they don't change to that exquisite white, luxurious coat until their parents turn at the first fall snows.

The air was white with thousands of arctic terns; you could scarcely walk without stepping on their eggs, laid every few feet, or yards, in the short, prickly maritime grass. All the eggs seemed to be single here, though ordinarily two or even three are found in a set. The late golden sunlight so intensified the graceful gray, slim bodies, the long forked tails, black caps, scarlet feet and bills, that they looked like clouds of dazzling fairies. Amazing how anything as exquisite to the eye can be as hideous to the ear. Not a single place in the short arctic summer seems complete without them, soaring throughout storm or sunshine all day high and low, and during most of the bright night hours; leaving again so soon to fly over trackless oceans to another summer thousands upon thousands of miles away in the Antarctic.

The terns dived on us. But most of all they dived at the little arctic foxes, each of whom, a fluffy ball of fury, bounced immediately into the air, barking excitedly and snapping viciously at every bird which came his way. It was a fascinating sight. And it was obvious too that the foxes of this small isolated world live high in summer on tern and duck eggs; we saw several eating eggs in the distance. They must live also on mice or lemmings, though there were no fresh mice signs. Old holes and runways indicated their presence at certain periods.

Eric and Tommy Roe did the supper getting — a stew of bully beef, onions, bacon, and potatoes cooked over a small driftwood fire. More than merely appetizing smells of stew and driftwood penetrated the still, delicious air while Doc, Sue, and I rushed about frantically trying for pictures of foxes and terns.

Except for a short line of low willows some three to four-feet high in its center, Fox Island is completely open. Its sandy pebbly soil is covered with a silver-green sea grass with broadish leaves and barley-type head, mixed with buttercup species, saxifrages, a Pyrola, and a tiny Botrychium fern. Savannah sparrows, semipal plovers, least sandpipers, and willow ptarmigan were all fairly common. Small flocks of old-squaws and mergansers, a few Canada geese, and female eiders were coming into a small fresh water pond which lay in a shallow depression. Beyond this, on the south side of the island, were several largish pools, both fresh water and brakish, surrounded by bright green, miniature swampy meadows covered with little Habenaria orchids and wild sweet peas.

In addition to the supper stew, like the foxes, we tried eating tern eggs. They're about the size of a bantam's and, if one were hungry enough, doubtless these would be a delicate morsel. But they have a very gamey, distinctly undomesticated flavor. After supper when the others wandered off, I sat by the fire talking to Tommy Roe. He was a gold mine of information about this country. So much of an Eskimo's life must depend on his understanding of natural history and his ability to use it properly, in the broadest sense of that phase, for his own welfare.

Poise and pride and complete self-reliance from knowledge acquired out of lonely encounters with the ofttimes terrible forces of the North were written clearly on Tommy's face. The dark skin and chubby features were of no importance at all compared to the character and expression that were there. Watching his face made me suddenly particularly dislike smooth, sophisticated countenances in our part of the world. Despite their ability at times to be uproariously gay, men up here have a deeper gravity than ours — they seem somehow far more grown-up. Although Tommy is so young, perhaps in his mid-twenties, all of us, even Eric, looked to him throughout our entire trip for undisputed leadership.

Here are some of the many interesting things he told me: Lands he has seen away north (he must mean north of Hudson Bay, I think) have high mountains rising out of the sea. They are white with snow and waterfalls, with flat places "just full right up with flowers" in summertime. There are hardly any flies there — maybe a few days or a week is all. And I would like it there. "There are so many animal. Walrus just all over the sea; and wolf calling; polar bear sometime like gold and big as whales!" (Several bearskins we've seen at Churchill have been more cream than pure white; one in the Hobsons' measured nine feet from nose to tail tip.)

Southern fox forms like the red and silver and cross are beginning to work farther north so that Tommy has wondered if they will some day drive out the less aggressive, gentle little white foxes. For the past year or two there has been a real scarcity of the latter; Tommy had to give up trapping for a time and come "far south" to get work. Churchill is the farthest south he has ever been. (Coming south to Churchill is a fascinating point of view!)

Since foxes depend a lot on lemmings, when the lemming grow scarce, as they do about every four years or so, foxes migrate.

"Foxes follow wolve and bear, away out on the ice," said Tommy. "Chase 'em for the bodies of animal like caribou and seal they leaves around. Sometime they trails a polar bear days and days, miles out from shore. . . . One time I count twenty-three white foxes round a dead whale on shore."

I tried to tell him how I *hate* the thought of trapping for the suffering it causes to both mind and body of an animal. . . .

Tommy answered, "Foxes caught in winter don't suffer too long maybe. When weather's cold they lose sense in a few hours and die in a night. Warm days is the bad time to trap. I can't stomach that a lot o' times. . . ."

In a good year, with reasonable luck and skill, a man may catch $1000 worth of white foxes. Occasionally someone gets $3000 worth of skins in a year. But in the lean years, when there are few foxes, a trapper may make little or nothing at all. It takes "a many year" to see whether a man can be rich or poor from trapping foxes.

Large furs like caribou, polar bear, wolf, and seal are most valuable, but arctic foxskins are by far the most important and widely traded. Trappers also get wolverine (prized as a trimming for hoods since it frosts over around the face much less readily than other furs), weasels, and arctic hares.

What Tommy Roe said of trapping is more or less corroborated by other trappers around Churchill. But Tommy, an Eskimo, took all my questions concerning trapping most seriously and returned careful and studied answers. Is this because he's an unusual individual, or because his people who have been in these lands so long have a better, more thorough knowledge of the importance of animal behavior and the Eskimo equivalent of conservation?

Tommy was deeply interested in the story of the Alaskan bear trapper, notorious for cruelty and carelessness, who, after having been caught and mangled in his own huge bear set, never again trapped even the smallest creature.

Terry and Ronnie and Eric think, with justice, that my knowledge of trapping is far too meager. Or perhaps they just don't want to think deeply into something which has been to them a profitable way of life. (Eric and Ronnie are apt merely to make annoyingly flippant remarks concerning my "felicitous" combination of grave and gay — to which *I* can only retort on their felicitous choice of words. . . .)

You can't start out to argue convincingly against a business so vitally important to both trapper and trader throughout all the vast North. Besides I think you must recognize that the *good* trapper or trader is a real conservationist. He has to be for the sake of his future livelihood. But I continue to wonder why the anti-trapping and conservation leagues, in addition to educational and propaganda material, don't expend greater time and energy on the discovery and invention of humane methods of trapping? Every so often something crops up concerning a new trap or method that kills as it catches, but this seldom seems to attract sufficient attention or careful investigation.

Later in the evening I went with Eric to see if fox cubs (we never saw the parents the whole time we were on the island) were still around a den by the northeast shore. There wasn't a sign, so we strolled on around a mile of beach. It was 10 P.M.; the terns had quieted. It was absolutely still and clear and warm. There was nothing but sky and sea, our flat little island, the slightest bit of something solid in the midst of it all. The deep uniform blue of air and water had paled — one could barely distinguish sky from sea — to a light pink, misty silver and lavender. That warm, deeply radiant golden glow (I think its like can be found only in arctic places), which had enveloped the tranquil world for hours and hours, was replaced gradually and imperceptibly by a pale, silvery-yellow from a full moon mirrored completely in the perfectly calm water. It was still daylight, just a softer mellower daylight, and the moon seemed merely to have changed places with the sun.

More seaweed was strewn around these shores than at Churchill. As we looked back over it into the northwest (in summer here the sun keeps always in the northern sky) with the low sunset light passing directly through it, for an instant it turned a sudden, sparkling, ruby red. The beach looked heaped with jewels. It was so surprising and so breathtakingly beautiful — as though it suddenly had been bewitched.

I'd forgotten (almost!) that Eric was there till he said, "Exactly like 'lovely as a Lapland night' isn't it?" Oddly enough these very words of Wordsworth had been running in my head all evening and now for the first time I completely understood their meaning. Before, I've associated them solely with that lovely person, our great-granny Elizabeth, who at the age of ninety-four seemed to die with the beauty of both body and mind so undimmed.

> Thy thoughts and feelings shall not die,
> Nor leave thee when grey hairs are nigh,
> A melancholy slave;
> But an old age serene and bright,
> And lovely as a Lapland night,
> Shall lead thee to thy grave.

What a contradictory person Eric is. I shall never understand him. At first that evening I felt as though I hated anyone else at all to be with me in such a setting; then he seemed, after all, just the right one to be there. Eric and Ronnie are tremendous readers. Eric in particular — though I don't suppose he's cultured in the conventional sense — seems to have a surprising, if scattered, knowledge of literature. His uncle's house, he said once, was crammed with books from garret to cellar; one couldn't escape reading.

One of Eric's most impressive characteristics is, I believe, an ability to be serenely at home with any kind of person in any kind of setting. He can associate intimately with Tommy Roe (or any other nice Eskimo) with as much pleasure as if he were his best friend — Ronnie for example. Not because Tommy is, or is not, an Eskimo, but simply because he's a satisfactory and interesting individual. If Eric were to turn up in striped pants at a royal garden party in London (though I much prefer him in his Hudson Bay costume of aged gray flannels, odorous black sweater, and flannel shirt), he'd be equally poised and comfortable. Whereas one can't imagine Horace in either situation! He'd be courteous and considerate and dignified, but definitely not happy. Especially Horace couldn't be pals with an Eskimo or an Indian or a tart. He'd love to feed and clothe them and aid their morals, but he'd never really get next to their minds and characters. I have a hunch that if men like Eric were to hold influential positions as well as people like my dear, charitable, public-spirited New England relatives, there would be a greater understanding of human problems. But people like Eric just never do. Perhaps they're too selfish, too knowledgeable, too egotistical —

Sue and I had put our sleeping bags, well protected by netting, for mosquitoes were rather bad when the breeze died, near a fox den in the center of the island. And for hours, through that serene and bright and lovely "Lapland night," three cubs like graceful kittens played beside the holes a few yards away, or sidled up to sniff our netting. We practically took them to bed with us. It was so enthralling we couldn't close our eyes till finally the babies disappeared down their holes.

Lying directly beneath the sky in that exquisite light, in that great, utterly remote and untouched world, was the most perfect experience I've ever had. Up here where the earth is so free of man you get, oddly enough, a truer perspective of man.

I wanted to keep awake to experience every minute of the night. But I slept soundly for several hours and didn't wake till it was bright, early morning. Terns were screaming again and the instant I stuck my head out of the netting, dove at me and spotted everything with droppings. Sue, and the men farther over near the shore, all seemed sound asleep, so I went for a morning dip in the little pond. It was shallow and cold and mosquitoes were about, but it felt wonderful.

There were no signs of foxes. After spending so much of the night up and about, like the people of Churchill, they were all sleeping in.

I started back and met Eric hunting firewood. He asked if I'd enjoyed my "bathe" and when I looked at him coldly said, "Didn't I see you stripping over by the pond a while ago?" Just when I think he's wonderful, full of noble thoughts, he says or does something hateful!

I spent the morning on my own exploring the south shore of Fox Island. In a patch of the silver grass an old-squaw flushed off her nest. It was the prettiest thing. A clutch of eight, pale tan eggs were wrapped in a thick blanket of the softest little gray and black breast feathers — an exquisite down quilt, light as air and so hot it heated my cold hand up the instant I placed it underneath. No wonder mother ducks can wander off and have their eggs kept warm and safely incubating under such a cover.

Reposing in sandy mud against a boulder in the midst of miles of flats uncovered by low tide wouldn't be considered blissful ordinarily. But it was. There was one rock just big enough to shade my body — the only shade anywhere for endless miles — and there were no mosquitoes. I lay on my raincoat and had a wonderful nap.

By afternoon hazy lines of clouds were beginning to dim the sky a little, and a stiff easterly breeze had come up. "Change o' weather," said Tommy Roe noncommittally. "Best be moving on our way back the coast. Storm'll be getting up and there's an awful lot o' ice out there. . . ."

The fond thoughts we'd had of going on right to Cape Churchill, if we got caribou or seal to supplement our food, were reluctantly abandoned. We were off as soon as the canoe, which for hours had been grounded high and dry by low tide a half mile from the waterline, was afloat again. And when we got out from the island a bit we were in rough water. The canoe hit the top of each wave with an awful whack and everyone and everything, except Eric crouched under the bow, was drenched every other minute. Tommy's brown and rosy face, streaming with salt water, never lost that engaging grin as he worked over his engine, kept the boat unfailingly into the center of each wave crest and bailed endlessly. Doc Carey, gray hair on end (*actually* unshaved), for once really dirty and messy and jolly, laughed aloud when a wave hit especially hard. I've never liked him so much.

As we peered out under a rubber poncho between salt shower baths, we saw, about ten feet above us, a pair of butterflies — a species of silver spot, which is apparently the most common kind up here thus far. What on earth were they doing out over the sea several miles from land? They must have been blown by the

wind to a watery grave; but we began presently to see
that their flight was far from aimless. They kept steadily abreast of our canoe; a wind blowing heavily against
starboard didn't phase them at all — frail tiny things,
about the size of rose petals.

The wind got higher; still the butterflies kept with us.
The outboard was frequently suspended in the air
where it roared alarmingly, and Eric got out his paddle.
It had all been so exhilarating up to then, and the sun
was still so warm despite the haze, I hadn't really
thought much about danger. But if Tommy relaxed his
vigilance a second, or the engine gave out. . . . The
water of Hudson Bay is so icy one can't survive in it
long. And there would be no human help to be had
here. Even as I thought this Tommy yelled something
at Eric, we swerved suddenly toward the left, tipping
heavily and awash on one side, and were heading diagonally toward the coast about a mile distant. At last
we landed, banging against boulders which Eric, jumping out in water to his waist, just kept us off. It was a
shallow cove somewhat northeast of the long point
from which we'd watched the caribou.

The butterflies, having traveled about eight miles
across open sea in a wind so strong a man at times could
hardly stand in it, sometimes steering right against it,
landed with us, fluttered gaily off over the flower-

bedecked tundra, and disappeared. Even the most learned member of our party, Doc C., was nonplussed and couldn't account for this phenomenon. It was utterly miraculous that those tiny creatures could do such a thing.

"Had to head in," remarked Tommy Roe casually, squeezing salt water off dripping legs and arms. "Wind too high. Couldn't make it if we'd went a foot further. When wind dies in the morning, try again. Best go back when we can. . . ."

"Oh well," said Dr. Carey easily, "now we can always hike back. We're only about twenty miles or so from Churchill?"

"About three times as far by land," Eric answered grimly. "And some going over muskeg and mud flats. We've not much food either unless we get a deer or something." ("Deer" up here invariably means caribou.)

However, the arctic summer's day was yet young, the hazy sun was warm, a heavy sea wind blew off mosquitoes, there was new territory to examine. Tommy and Eric, with the rifle, vanished in the direction of the low ridge over which our caribou had gone, and the rest of us explored.

All the little lakes just here were long and very narrow, lying north and south as did the long low ridges which formed the point. These gradually petered out some distance inland where faint lines of small trees began. It was the drier type of tundra — lovely to walk on — and the whole world was simply rose-pink with dwarf rhododendron. There were those single, clear, silvery alarm notes of golden plovers, wild cries of curlews and other birds typical of the open tundra at Churchill.

On our way back to build the fire and add a few remaining vegetables to the stew of the day before (Sue and I thought it our turn to get supper), we met Tommy and Eric also returning — without a caribou. Apparently the caribou had left the region. Just at that instant by a little lake we flushed a female eider from her young, and Eric promptly shot her. He went to pick her up and Tommy said, his face so blank and expressionless that it was more forbidding than a string of curses, "Too bad that — to shoot a mother bird . . ." (You always hate Eric in his ruthless moments, but I must admit that the poor duck added greatly to our supper stew, and the babies were big enough perhaps to care for themselves, or join a brood of another mother. Rafts composed of many broods of many mothers often are observed in the North.)

In the late evening, Dr. C. and Sue and I walked some miles eastward to extensive mud flats toward which great flocks of birds had been flying. By that time the sky was completely overcast and it was darker than usual — odd, lavender twilight lit by the moon behind clouds. Small rocks were like black, crouching animals scattered about in the acres and acres of vast, bright, silvery sheets of mud. And the whole place was teeming with feeding shore birds — hundreds upon hundreds of them. Their voices filled the world. Herring and Bonaparte gulls, terns, Hudsonian godwits, eiders, old-squaws, pintails, many kinds of plover and sandpiper, turnstones, dowitchers, and others which Dr. C. didn't recognize. It was wonderful beyond description.

We had lovely beds that night on firm, springy moss (rather different from the hard, cold sand of Fox Island). After a few hours of the night before, we were sleeping like the dead when — "Wake up, girls, wake up. We've got to go — storm's coming — *Hurry*, get your things together — "

It seemed to me I'd only just gotten to sleep and Dr. Carey's voice had been irritating me in a dream for ages.

From the depths of her sleeping bag Sue growled, "What in heck's the matter? I don't see any storm. It's only two o'clock. Tommy said we shouldn't start before five anyway — "

It certainly was a nasty-looking dawn: a murky dirty

tan and pale yellow under a dense gray sky. There seemed no wind. The sea looked like solid silver. Down on the beach over a feeble fire, Dr. Carey was holding the pot with the last dregs of the stew, while Tommy and Eric worked grimly to get the canoe across half a mile of mud as it was still partly low tide. Who wanted very stale, half-cold stew at 2 A.M. anyway when one was half sick from being waked like that! But goodness knew when we could eat again.

Sue said, "If a storm's coming why don't we stay here for heaven's sake? It would be a lot safer."

"No food, no shelter," said Doc Carey gloomily. "They think we can make it if we start now. Hope they're right. . . ."

Finally we got our stuff hauled out to the canoe across the great expanse of sticky mud and were off, heading out into a queer, almost completely colorless, world of sky and sea. After we got beyond the point we struck big, oily, unpleasant-feeling swells. Very different from the cheerful, boisterous, blue-green waves of the afternoon before.

Then looking out at eiders through the glasses I saw something which gave me a sudden cold feeling: Ice. Not picturesque, isolated, little bergs and ice pans but a great solid white line of it. Because it had been more or less absent in the vicinity of Fox Island, I'd sort of forgotten about it. Now I realized how fast the wind was moving it in.

What was it the H.B. man at Churchill had said? "Just watch out for ice if wind changes so it won't close in on you some place you can't land — but Tommy won't let that happen. He's a good lad. Knows his ice, he does. . . ."

We passed the caribou cove which looked grim and bleak and deserted. The engine kept having fluttering spells, but Tommy always got it started again. Dr. Carey and Sue looked awfully gray; perhaps it was the cold stew, or perhaps it was only the light. But I thanked the Lord for my usually stable stomach at sea, and all the sailing we've always done.

Gosh! Now the engine had stopped again and this time it wouldn't start. Eric paddled steadily, keeping the bow into the waves. But after unintelligible remarks between him and Tommy, he handed his paddle to us with a brief, "Keep her head on as much as you can," and climbed cautiously over us back to stern giving me a reassuring pressure as he passed. He somehow gives one a sense of strength and complete resourcefulness; the conviction that if anyone can, he will pull through a crisis.

With intense concentration he and Tommy worked over the engine, one or the other steadily paddling stern with powerful, skillful strokes. They were two equally thrilling figures somehow — one an Eskimo, the other a Danish Englishman. It's odd what an appeal physical strength has for one up here — so much more deep an appeal than athletic feats for instance. Physical strength here is used for absolutely vital things; and it isn't just physical — it has to be combined with grit and character and hard-won knowledge. Sue and Doc Carey and I took turns paddling bow. But despite our efforts, sometimes the canoe, a mere nutshell in those waves, tipped alarmingly; we were drifting slowly toward a solid rocky shore and the ice field seemed closing in. We couldn't land there. *Why* hadn't this happened opposite the Cove? There was an angry, dull red glow where the sun was supposed to be and spatters of rain. We seemed to be drifting for hours, but suddenly Eric got the engine going again. Everyone thought "Thank God," and Sue and Doc and I crouched down under the poncho once more. It was very nastily cold and wet.

At last we could see that particularly long stretch of gravel beach before the rock ledges toward Churchill begin. Wind was getting up, waves bigger, the ice surely closer. We ought to land, we said. Yes, Tommy was heading in; he and Eric were shouting and pointing at the ice. No, we were heading out again.

Suddenly Doc Carey's head, like a tortoise popping

out of its shell, appeared above the poncho. "Why didn't you land on that beach there? We have no business to go on in this —"

Eric said coldly, "That ice's not so bad — It's broken up ahead. Churchill's only a short way now. Tommy says we can make it."

We were off the Rock Ridge. In the high waves and mist it looked black and high and dangerous, very unlike the place I've so rejoiced in, and napped on, and bathed on. Now we were steering carefully through ice pans. We'd soon be through. No, there was a solid bank ahead. We were cut off. We'd *have* to turn back. We *couldn't* turn back. Solid ice behind.

I'm not sure whether I prayed. I think I kept saying "God. . . ." Suddenly ice just ahead seemed to open up, or perhaps the small opening had been there all along. We went straight through. There was the mission tower and the beach back of the café. There were rough breakers but Tommy, probably by miraculous skill, got us in just right and Eric leapt in water as we went up the beach on a wave. . . .

Well, that was only yesterday, and I'm safe and dry in the tent. (Did I once think this tent alarmingly remote and beset by dangers?!) And now we're contemplating another trip.

Nine

SUE HAS HAD AN ADVENTURE! Sensible, capable, self-reliant Susan who *"never* acts on rash impulses and sudden enthusiasms," which get her into trouble like Rosamund. For some days she's been mentioning, off-handedly, something about going up the river with a rugged chap, one Brown, to see reported nesting grounds of a big concentration of geese. But I've been plant collecting so intensively lately and have seen her so little, I didn't pay much attention.

Yesterday Doc Carey reported that she'd gone off somewhere at an early hour. And she didn't appear again till long past our usual suppertime at the café, when she was more than noncommittal about her day and any geese she'd seen. That sparkling mien of hers was completely subdued. You couldn't say she looked pale under all that tan, but she *acted* pale. After she'd eaten a small part of a large, indigestible platter saved by Terry, who simply loves her, she and I walked out to the beach and the instant we were out of sight she sat down flat and said,

"Oh Lord, what a fool I was! To think I could ever be such a fool. . . ."

"Sue, what on earth. . . .? Where *have* you been anyway?'"

Well, it transpired that Brownie, a short, tough, wiry man, attractive in a sort of free and easy way, whose winter trapping cabin is on a stream some miles up the river, had invited Sue to go there with him. He told her a lot of geese had been nesting in marshes nearby. There *were* a lot of geese, sure enough, both young and old, though all Canadas and no rare species as she'd hoped.

But when she went into the cabin with Brownie she found he expected her to do something very, very different from looking at wild geese with him. In fact he supposed that she had come for one express purpose and that geese were purely incidental. Apparently they were both equally flabbergasted — Sue absolutely horrified, Brownie (fortunately) excessively hurt. After a few attempts at persuasion (into the fascinating details of which Sue would not go), which she repulsed by the amazing counterpersuasion that he was a "gentleman," he brought her home again — unscathed!

Terence, to whom under a vow of strict secrecy I

related a little of this, was alarmingly furious — at Sue chiefly, for not consulting him. Apparently Brownie's the one trapper she shouldn't have gone out with. Terry's beetling brows stuck out like a snowdrift, those blue eyes flashed sparks, and that nose of his was absolutely purple. I thought he'd start out for Brownie that second and beat him to a pulp.

Incidentally, both Sue and I've had some fascinating proposals to remain up here, so if we don't come home. . . . Imagine Horace, let alone the family, if I married a trapper. I shall not mention names, but suffice it to say that they were not from the intelligentsia group. There certainly are, as Sue puts it, trappers *and* trappers — We have each, for example, been asked to marry someone or just live with him for an indefinite period, sharing fur profits 50-50; and — the most unique proposition of all — both of us were invited to spend the winter with one man, at the end of which period we would each receive a third of the profits. These, and a few other quaint propositions, have been largely tendered through Terry. But one, to his absolutely scandalized amusement, was via Dr. Carey.

The Churchill inhabitants appear now to be convinced of the ruggedness of our physical constitutions at least. What our actual reputations with the less intelligent are, heaven alone knows. I don't suppose they take seriously for an instant all this chasing about with butterfly nets, cameras, and plant presses.

We've been trying to obtain permission to go with the H.B.C. schooner, *Fort Severn,* due to sail soon for Eskimo Point some hundred and sixty miles on up the coast, but the powers-that-be either can't or won't consent. They're not allowed to take ordinary passengers, it's too tough a trip for young ladies, if we wanted to go in a scientific capacity we should have discussed the matter in Winnipeg at headquarters before we came up, and so on. It is maddening. We've hoped so much to get even farther north, but since this one boat is the only means of going there it looks as though we must just give up the whole idea.

It is July 20th and the summer season is far advanced; yet here and there are odd reminders of both spring and fall as well. East winds still blow ice floes of late spring in from the sea. Pink fireweed, golden rods, and asterlike flowers associated with autumn, make splashes of color everywhere over rock and tundra. Birds are flocking together for southern migrations.

Flower succession has followed flower succession. Rose and white and yellow waves of willows and rhododendrons, buttercups and saxifrages of late June and early July gave way to waves of purple-pink vetch, *Hedysarum mackenzii,* exquisite, delicate flower clusters with a marvelous odor that reminds one of orchids and gardenias and tropical things; and perfect clouds of avens or Dryas, single white blossoms with huge gold centers. The Dryas covers the landscape and carpets with white and gold, the sandy dunes east of the Rock Ridge, right down to the blue sea. There are very delicate little rose-pink primroses set charmingly along rock ledges; the single flower of the butterwort, Pinguicula, like a large bright violet rising from a rosette of yellow-green leaves, seems especially lovely in this land where pure blue and purple flowers are rare. There are quantities of louseworts and vivid patches of Indian paintbrush in white and scarlet and pink and yellow.

Why go south to the "Land of Flowers" if you could watch an arctic tundra spread for a thousand, thousand miles with blossoming quilts and carpets?

We've been spending time lately back at the timber-line — a region of scrubby spruce and larch, lakes and marshy ponds. Except that it too is utterly wild and un-touched, it lacks the lure and gripping charm of open tundra and coastline. But small bright pools of sunlight mixed with black shadows of thick trees are restful after the unadulterated brilliance outside. And little muskeg patches are snowed-over completely with cotton grass whose great, soft, white, satiny heads are beginning now to fluff out in all their glory. When sun catches them, it looks as though sparkling drifts had been scattered in the midst of a dark forest. To the naturalist this region is interesting, too, because of the quite different, more southern types of plant and animal life — many Hudsonian, almost Canadian, zonal forms instead of the arctic and subarctic around Churchill and the open tundra. In the woods great beds of lush sphagnum moss and lichens cover the ground. There are *Lycopodium annotinum,* and various orchids; the most beautiful, the little Franklin's lady's-slipper, *Cypripedium passerinum,* first collected by the Dr. Richardson of Sir John Franklin's journey to the Polar Seas in 1819-1822. The little, white, oval, slipper-shaped flower, dotted with purple spots, was supposed to resemble a sparrow's egg. Hence the passerinum. There are also other orchids — coral root, *Corallorhiza trifida,* Habenarias, and *Orchis rotundifolia.* There is a wild currant, many Pyrolas (including the *Moneses uniflora*), *Shepherdia canadensis, Galium boreale, Linnaea borealis,* anemones, and other species all typical of more temperate regions.

The woods abound with chimes of gray-cheeked thrushes, those striking clear whistles, on a sort of minor note, of Harris's sparrows, redpolls and black-poll warblers; and above all that lovely, clear, joyous, "Sweet, sweet, sweet, where are you sweet?" of the big, beautiful, red-brown fox sparrow. A couple of weeks ago we were much elated to find the nest of a Harris's sparrow in a gravelly bank under a clump of Labrador tea. (Labrador tea incidentally, is said to make a rather bitter-tasting drink but is useful as a throat and chest remedy, or for the tannin used by Russians for tanning leather.) The Harris's sparrow (the sexes look alike and are hard to distinguish) is surely a handsome creature with its dense black head and throat, large cream-colored bill, and body marked in rich browns, whites, and blacks. Though common up here, the Harris's sparrow is a rare bird as yet in collections. The eggs actually were discovered only a few years ago.*

Timber ponds and swampy places are full of coots and snipe and rusty blackbirds. The larger lakes have pintails and mergansers, arctic loons, and occasional pairs of wild geese with yellow, downy young. Every isolated clump of tall black spruce possesses a pair of lesser yellow-legs teetering dizzily on the topmost twigs (ridiculous perch for a long-legged shore bird), looking ready to fall at any second, making a deafening noise. The instant you're discovered by a yellow-legs it's good-

* Although a nest and young of Harris's sparrow was found in 1907 by E. T. Seton, in Last Woods, the eggs of this sparrow were not found until Dr. George M. Sutton discovered them at Churchill in 1931.

by to chances of making a quiet approach on anything. Some birds are awfully like some people.

There're numerous colonies of the pretty little white Bonaparte's gulls with their black heads and reddish feet. If you get anywhere near a nest fifteen or twenty feet up in a spruce, your life and comfort aren't worth a thing. They dive on you in screaming clouds and shower you with droppings. The other day one struck my head so sharply, I've hardly been able to bear a hat since.

Another day I had the fascinating experience of assisting a baby pintail into the world. An area I like especially, not far inside timberline, contains numerous small lakes winding all about and connecting with each other. You can always hear in the distance the melodious honking of geese. I found a pintail's nest well concealed in spagnum moss under a little larch covered with bright green feathery foliage and tiny new rose-colored cones. The nest contained seven greenish-tan eggs, deliciously warm wrapped in their thick down blanket. Several were just ready to hatch — actually you could hear the babies inside pecking at the shells. One in particular was snapping his bill, peeping and pecking at a tremendous rate. The shells are so tough it takes a long time to get through, but finally he worked his head out, blinked, took a rest, peeped, and began struggling again. I assisted somewhat, now and again pulling away pieces of shell, and at last he emerged, darling and fluffy, much less damp than I expected, quite wide-awake and knowledgeable, into the big world. Next day four more eggs had hatched. One baby had his bill out at 11 A.M., but was in the same position still when I looked again at three in the afternoon. The following morning all were hatched and gone. I hunted on nearby ponds but there wasn't a sign.

All of us have been visiting extensively with a pair of arctic loons, whose nest Sue found on a tiny island providentially close to the shore of a large lake. The blind, set in the most uncomfortable spot of wet, unstable muskeg yet discovered, tipping practically into the water, affords the most marvelous, intimate view of the loons and their nest just ten feet away. It takes the loons twenty to forty-five minutes to become accustomed to anyone in the blind, even when one of us tucks the other inside and walks conspicuously off.

The first day at the end of an hour of agonized squatting in ice-cold muck, I was about to give up when a voice, so hollow and ghostly I jumped and nearly spoiled everything by shaking the whole blind, sounded right in my ear. And then a gorgeous velvet gray-black-and-white-clad creature, two feet long, with a deep red eye, drifted from right beside the blind slowly, slowly up to the island. Must have swum underwater a long way to get there without my seeing it. With a series of agonizingly awkward heaves and jumps (the legs of a loon are so far back on the body it can scarcely move at all on land), it pulled itself onto the loose platform of mud and sticks which forms the nest, and began at once, with its long strong bill, to push and roll two big olive-green eggs down between its legs to the brood spot. This is the only place where eggs can obtain sufficient warmth to be incubated, for the loon's whole breast is insulated completely with the densest, most efficient coat of thick little feathers.

The entire process is the most wonderful sight. I hope the loons won't be scared away at our continual and fascinated stares. There is always that sudden ghastly, ghostly, yet beautiful voice, the phantomlike approach (you never know the bird is there till it's directly beside you), the queer agonized waddling on the nest, the correct, fussy placing of eggs, and the gradual settling down of the great big, handsome creature looking straight at you with those red jewel eyes.

The Hudsonian godwit is an interesting bird which Sue and I had never seen before. A large shore bird with gray-brown back, a lovely brownish-red breast, and tail ringed with black and white, its long bill instead of curving down like the curlew's, turns slightly up. And, though ornithologists have taken a female at Churchill containing eggs in the ovaries and observed immature birds, the only nesting localities ever officially reported have been in the Anderson and Mackenzie River regions. Actual eggs and nests of the Hudsonian godwit have yet to be discovered.

Each time one of us sees a pair of godwits fussing about — they are always fussing about with incessant loud, emphatic scold notes something like a robin's — he thinks if *I* should be the one to find the nest. . . .*

Out of a brood of seven little red-breasted mergansers, one day we collected three for Sue to make up. I have never seen anything so adorable. Baby sandpipers and young ducks and geese are the softest, prettiest things, but these baby mergansers — they feel and look exactly as if they were covered with man-made velvet; they have pure white breasts, dark backs, each with six little patches of white, bright reddish areas on either side of the throat, long, deep orange bills, orange feet. Sue skinned them, stuffed and fluffed them, and sewed them up so beautifully, that not a single

* Miss Hazel R. Ellis, Professor of Biology at Keuka College, with the aid of U. S. entomologist, W. O. McDuffe, who had found a nest without identifying it, was able to report and photograph the actual nest, eggs, and young of the Hudsonian godwit at Churchill in June 1948.

person who sees them can be restrained from fondling and cuddling them and exclaiming. They form a regular exhibition for Churchill.

Surely baby mergansers were designed to give the utmost in pleasure. In a wilderness again and again (somehow you see more readily the beauty there than in man's creations, though they possess it too), whether it be mirages or auroras, white whales or baby mergansers, you recall the philosophy of so many of the great scientists and explorers: Like a comforting, continuous strand it runs ever through their thoughts that somehow, always, there *is* definite purpose and beneficence in the great, creative, underlying force of all things.

Sue and Doc and I go all day often without seeing each other. Imagine the strangeness and relaxation of eight hours straight without sight of another human being — your thoughts and actions and observations all your own. I'm just beginning really to comprehend that faraway, wise, contented sort of look in a northerner's eye when he speaks of being "alone."

When I'm not too far inside timberline I reserve the afternoon for a leisurely return along the Rock Ridge. Because I love this area most of all — the closeness to the sea world, the exquisite, brilliant tundra gardens scattered all through the rocks, the lovely bathtub pools, the pure physical comfort of it compared with muskeg and tundra and timber. And there are always endless interesting and varied things to watch.

One day I discovered a pipit's nest — the only one we've found. These slender, pale buff and olive-brown streaked wagtails, that resemble larks, are common on ledges where they run along wagging their tails frantically, just as they do on mountains above timberline in our country. But they're very secretive about nests. Again and again I've been sure I'd discovered one, only to have the bird flush and slip out of sight so suddenly that I lost track of where she'd come from.

This time I saw the exact spot but the pipit vanished before I could get even a glimpse of the two white tail feathers, one of the chief distinguishing field marks. I had to go away and return later and flush it all over again to be able to say I'd definitely identified a pipit.

The pretty, little, grass-lined nest, containing three tiny naked babies, was against the side of a rock in the midst of crowberry which hung over so thickly it completely obscured it.

I've always considered the pipit a bit of a dull bird both as to voice and appearance. It wasn't till I'd observed them here that I realized they can sing exquisitely. They start on a series of notes more or less on the same pitch. They keep on with this so long you'd never dream there is anything else, until suddenly, from way high up in the air like a skylark, it dissolves in a shower of ecstatic, warbling, charming notes.

I trust Bill, after this dissertation, will be more respectful of pipits. I seem to recall that the name "pipit" inspired him, as well as others I could mention, with most unseemly mirth. Godwit and bristle-thighed curlew are the two that intrigue me. I'd no idea that the latter was a real-live bird when I heard of it first.*

The day of finding the pipit's nest was a good one, for I saw two weasels. Though trappers report them as common around their winter camps, we haven't seen them here before. About the size of red squirrels, though more slender and elongated, with the same red-brown fur, they were playing in a mossy hollow of the Rock Ridge. One was heavy and fat, the other much slimmer and smaller (the male perhaps?). They jumped about this way and that as lightly and gracefully as leaves blown in a wind. They chased each other, and sat up to stare showing creamy underparts,

* In June 1948, north of the Yukon River, Alaska, Dr. A. A. Allen, and his son David Allen, discovered for the first time the nest of the bristle-thighed curlew, so called for the strange bristlelike feather formation on its thighs. This curlew travels yearly all the way from Tahiti and the Society Islands of the Pacific to nest in western Alaska. This was the last North American species of bird whose nest and nesting habits were still completely unknown; Dr. Allen was awarded the Burr Prize of the National Geographic Society for this expedition. Arthur A. Allen, "The Curlew's Secret," *National Geographic* (Dec. 1948).

little whiskered faces, and black, wicked eyes bursting with curiosity. No wonder the trappers like to make pets of them and regard them with tolerance despite their thieving, mischievous propensities to run off with human property.

Sue and I have been seriously contemplating (Dr. C. wouldn't consider it even) a trip down the Churchill River, starting about thirty miles up, with Big Dan, an Icelandic carpenter. Dan is a quaint soul who does odd jobs around Sue's shack, the café, and elsewhere. He's as broad as he is long, extraordinarily light on his feet and a most expert person with either carpenter's tools or a boat and paddle. He spends hours discoursing on the bad qualities of the opposite sex. "Womens' dispositions is somethin' fierce," and he had to hunt a long while before he could find one mild enough natured to suit him. He actually has a wife (unusual for men in these parts) tucked away in The Pas or somewhere — she must be the last word in meekness. Dan appears, however, to be tolerant of Sue and me and even condescends to be amused at our "antics," as he terms them. He's been expecting a Winnipeg man, whom he's taken on trips before, to go down the Churchill River with him. In addition to an expert Indian paddler, Dan said he could take Sue and me along if we thought we could "stand it."

There's a long stretch of white water somewhere. "Sure tough on the nerve. Miles you go through white water, so fast you can't hardly breathe. Your canoe jump right up in the air. Banks go by so fast you can't see 'em —" Few people have ever been down it, and only one woman — taken by Dan and two other men. When they were halfway through and had entered a comparatively mild stretch, Dan looked to see how she was faring. And there she was in the bottom of the canoe stretched out in a dead faint. So, he "didn't have to worry about her the rest of the trip anyway!"

However, we have been spared (fortunately probably) having to make a decision, for the man from Winnipeg could not come after all. I wouldn't have had to make a decision — shooting rapids has been one of the secret dreams of my life — but I couldn't have gone without my wiser and more cautious pal.

But even if we didn't shoot the rapids we did get in a trip seven miles up the river to Mosquito Point. The day we were to start we arose at 3 A.M., but the trapper friend of Terry's, supposed to take us in his canoe, didn't show up. Philosophically we did things around Churchill till noon, when such a wind came up we couldn't go anyway. But that night at supper, served silently by Luke (he can't put on the fancy touches Terry does when he exerts himself, but he is really a much better, steadier cook), when we were thinking longingly and confidently of early bed, who should appear but Ronnie and Eric, the latter balancing an outboard on his shoulder.

They announced they'd got a canoe belonging to another white trapper, one Eskimo Pete, waiting down by the river; Eric had borrowed an outboard; now we could start. So accompanied this time by Dr. C. and sleeping bags, Sue and I, Ronnie, Eric, and Eskimo Pete embarked from the willow flats where the trappers' tents are. The evening was lighting up the big river; we proceeded straight up this time through a great school of whales (chasing and harpooning one which, in the wild excitement, got away), past the white dots of the Indian camp and the old Hudson's Bay post dim in the distance, past the bare, bleak shores of the subarctic world, back inland to the thick willow-swamp and forest country. We reached Mosquito Point, a slightly less thickly overgrown little promontory on the north river bank about 10:30, having safely negotiated some swift shallow water at the beginning of a stretch of small rapids, where we all worked hard paddling and pushing against the current to keep clear of dangerous rocks.

About fifty yards from shore, however, the canoe stuck on one and, to avoid ripping the bottom, we all had to get out in a hurry. Ronnie and Eric, wading in to their waists, kindly carried Sue and me to shore. They complained bitterly of our weight (Sue, slightly larger than I, is no great weight either), but they went a most unnecessarily long and circuitous route to reach dry land. And they got an unholy kick out of slipping and almost dropping us at intervals. No one offered to carry Dr. C., though he, poor dear, minded getting wet far more than we did.

Stretching back from Mosquito Point was a solid half mile of shoulder-high willows growing so densely and impenetrably together that it looked exactly as though you could walk right on top of them. In the distance was the deep black line of the spruce forest, just beside us the great river, narrower here, with shallow, swift stretches. It was all completely wild and desolate — wild in a quite different sense from the tundra and the sea — far less beautiful and colorful, but gripping in a way of its own and quite unlike any country we've yet seen.

I shall not go into the subject of insect life on this trip but Mosquito Point is correctly named. And anyone knows what that means in *this* country. Why should anybody put up with for a minute such a land of hellish pests? The mere fact that they do must illustrate how great is its lure.

There was a more than primitive man-built hovel, so small we could scarcely all get in it at once, where we cooked and ate a meal or two. But all of us, except Pete, slept out on the only open space anywhere: a tiny moss-covered rocky bluff looking over the river and a vast wilderness. This spot was exactly large enough to accommodate Dr. C., Eric, Ronnie, Sue, and myself all stretched like sardines side by side. Above the roar of mosquitoes (we were all under nets but a lot of insects got inside too). Ronnie and Eric snored placidly and steadily. Dr. C. snorted in uneasy starts and jerks. He continues still, bless his heart, to be futilely distressed by the frequent stark necessity in this life for ignoring conventions. Sue and I, of course, did not snore at all. . . .

The next day, efficiently aided by Ronnie and Eric, who are expert shots and very knowledgeable about the northern wilds, was spent bird and plant and insect collecting. Many of the more southern forms were common — rusty blackbirds, robins, fox sparrows, yellow warblers and, to Dr. C.'s and my joy, two plants we've not seen yet at timberline across the river — a northern violet, *Viola palustris,* and the *Caltha palustris,* or marsh marigold.

Eric and I had a delightful walk along a more open windy portion of the river bank. We saw enormous fresh wolfprints in the sand and found a gray-cheeked thrush's nest. He shot two pike, or jackfish, which we ate for supper and gave me excellent lessons in shooting. Eric can be the most companionable person I know. Incidentally, I've been helping Sue a bit to skin specimens and even collect small birds lately, so I'm not too bad a shot. She assists with the plants now and then.

Eskimo Pete spent the entire night and day in impenetrable clouds of smoke shut tight inside the cabin. He is a strange character reputed to be somewhat "bushed." He has a startling habit of jerking his head when he walks. He certainly had a queer glitter in his eye, or perhaps we imagined it as we saw him largely through tears; we wept incessantly in the acrid smoke. (It's difficult to decide which is worse — smoke or mosquitoes; protected by a head net, personally, I think I prefer the latter.) Apparently Pete never has a partner and lives a large part of every year completely alone off on the Barrens. When he first came up here years ago he spent a lot of time with Eskimos farther north (hence the name Eskimo Pete), various Eskimo wives being lent him from time to time in exchange for canned goods. During supper he regaled us, between violent coughs, with certain fascinating items of information:

The Eskimos lick their children's faces to clean them. You do the same to a pretty Eskimo girl when you want a place to kiss. When Pete starts off on his winter trapping exhibitions his grubstake consists solely of several dozen bottles of ketchup, twenty pounds of candy, a hundred pounds of flour and baked beans. One spring night up the coast he was waked by a polar bear pulling at his blankets. He took to the ice and ran round and round a big hummock so fast and so long that the bear got tired first. Ever since then he's been looking back over his shoulder; he just can't stop it.

After supper we left Mosquito Point (thankfully) and black clouds of insects — actually you had to push them with a paddle to see your way through — followed us all down the river to Churchill where they joined other black clouds already there. The sled dogs were in a pitiful state, those chained up without any shelter, rolling and howling all night in agony. Lying awake most of the night under my mosquito bar — the first time I've had to use it in the tent — and listening to the dogs was one of those times when I hated this country.

Then something always happens which makes me love it all again. One's feelings for this land are like its inhabitants — very good or very bad, never neutral or indifferent.

The evening after the Mosquito Point trip, I went into the café to find Terry and Ronnie and Eric all bent over a small, husky pup which had been hit by the dinkey. It was laid on a newspaper on the table (our supper preparations were completely forgotten), had a broken leg and serious cuts about head and neck. The little fuzzy thing was bleeding badly and hardly seemed to be breathing. The owner had thought it too much hurt to bother with, but Eric wouldn't hear of letting it go. It was he, who has had some experience in medicine apparently, who was doing the doctoring. He had set the broken leg, bound it in a splint and, when I arrived, was sewing up a big cut. Bent over the pup, utterly absorbed, his big, well-shaped hands remarkably skillful and gentle, his face was completely tender and pitying. It was a phase of Eric I've sensed occasionally — a complete contrast to the hardness and indifference that is there sometimes.

After it was fixed up, warm water and canned milk forced down its throat, the pup suddenly opened its eyes, quivered and whined. And Eric, gathering it up in his arms and gentling it like a child, carried it off home with him.

Now, a few days later, it's alive and happy, hobbling about on three legs, cuts and broken paw all healing nicely.

August

Ten

vvvvvvvvvvvvvvvvvvvvvvvvvvvvvvvvvv

AUGUST HAS BEGUN and insect life, thank God, definitely
has dwindled. Very stormy days for awhile— really wild
ones that lashed Hudson Bay into huge waves. Sue and
I've spent hours on the Ridge watching them, "wild
white horses," hurling themselves out of a leaden sky
and a leaden sea like fiends upon the rocks. One day
there was a rainbow, not an arc but a perfectly straight,
sharp, vertical line of angry, vivid colors, like a great
jeweled sword thrust menacingly deep into an inky sea.
A sign of bad arctic weather, Ronnie and Eric told us.
Sure enough it was a warning of an even worse storm
to follow.

We've become the greatest friends with the Leighs,
a couple who live beyond the wireless station. In summer Mr. Leigh works at the grain elevator. In the past
he's been connected with the H.B.C. and one or two
other outfits, but now during winter, he trades independently with the Eskimos. The Leighs' winter home

is several hundred miles up the coast near Ranken Inlet. A short, strong, man with steady, pale blue eyes, he has a face you trust the instant you see it. But Mrs. Leigh is the one I know best, for I've had long visits with her on rainy days. She sees you coming from far off, and has a quaint and heart-warming way, always, of running out of her tiny house and waving both arms violently. She's the rarest kind of person — small and rosy with short light hair, sort of merry and fresh with the strength that comes from successfully living a remarkable life in very unusual circumstances. She's wholly *real* — as so many of these northern women are — and she completely loves and comprehends this kind of world.

The Leighs have seven huge sled dogs, real beauties, handled and loved and considered in a way that it does my heart good to see. They are said to be the fastest and best-behaved team in Churchill; they make you realize what the husky dog, properly cared for, is meant to be. It was through stopping to admire the dogs one day that I got to know the Leighs. The dogs, as large as St. Bernards, have fierce, intelligent eyes, big and noble faces. Their great heads possess the smaller wolflike ears characteristic of huskies. Their soft, luxuriant fur must be a foot thick; they look good enough to hug. Mrs. Leigh, in fact, does hug them, laughing merrily when, standing with paws upon her shoulders, they tower above her and almost bear her to the ground. Two are nearly pure white, one black and white, the others white and gray. Though usually chained they're allowed to run free and exercise daily, and are gentle and obedient so that Mrs. Leigh handles them easily herself. (In winter, though, three or four at once are the most she can manage on the sled.) Each dog is on a long length of chain by a well-made kennel where it can shelter from sun and storms, and each has a rock pool or regularly filled water can within reach.

Mr. Leigh is another, at any rate, who feels strongly on the maltreatment of dogs. He knew all about the cases I've noticed; his pale eyes were black with anger when we talked about them. And he knows and loves the character of the true husky. The other evening he told us of a trapper, last winter, who was forced to bring his partner eighty miles on a dog sled down to the tiny hospital here. The partner, a big heavy man, was desperately ill; they tried to make a rush trip. Thirty miles from Churchill four of the dogs gave out completely from sheer exhaustion and injured feet. (Mr. Leigh ties felt pads on his dogs when they travel over rough ice.) But the lead dog, known throughout the Barrens country for his size and great character, carried on alone all the way into Churchill. The man was saved.

The dog collapsed in his harness and died at the hospital door.

The Leighs' tiny two-roomed house is no bigger than any other in Churchill, but it has just the few touches that many of these homes — rather unnecessarily bare or ugly it seems to me — lack entirely. The smallest, roughest, most unpretentious of living quarters *can* have charm and beauty. The Leighs built their home with a view straight out across Hudson Bay. A big window, directly on the sea with all its moods and colors, makes you feel as though you'd boarded a ship.

Out of this very window one day last December (the Leighs stayed in Churchill later than usual), Mrs. Leigh saw two great polar bears just below. Yellow-white against the snow and rough sea ice of Hudson Bay, they were ambling along shore in a queer, loose-jointed, yet somehow graceful manner, their small heads on the long snaky necks turning this way and that. They vaguely reminded her of gigantic weasels — there was the same creamy winter fur, the disproportionately long thick neck, little head and tiny ears. Later when she and Mr. Leigh examined the tracks they found a single footprint measured fourteen to sixteen inches long by twelve to fourteen inches wide.* Each winter polar

* Mrs. Eva Beckett described to the author similar experiences when she watched polar bears on the beach of Churchill in December 1949 and 1950.

bears are seen from time to time along this same shore.
I wish I could spend a winter in a shack up here. . . .

It makes you happy merely to step inside Mrs. Leigh's
shining rooms. There's always a dish of fresh tundra
flowers on the table; there's a "refrigerator" (a square
hole in the ground with its bottom on the ice) by the
door; choice books cover several shelves; there is just
the amount of furniture anyone needs to be comfortable
with.

When I think of the burden of our large plush houses
full of valuables and antiques, I want a house like Mrs.
Leigh's. If you're not completely surrounded by material possessions, and must depend rather on the natural world for inspiration, I wonder if you haven't a far
greater chance to acquire spiritual values?

Mrs. Leigh's winter home, she says, is bigger — it has
three rooms instead of two — because they must spend
a much larger part of the time indoors. People try to
commiserate with her on her desperately lonely life so
far off during the dark and icy months, and here she is
"usually loving every minute of it!" Lots of it hasn't
been easy. The few people of Ranken Inlet are
five miles away. And the adventures she's had and
the tales she can tell. . . . Snowed-in in their cabin in
eighty-mile gales, at 60 below. She's been stormbound
in tents and snow igloos; when their small son was only

four, they were lost in a storm once for days on the ice of Hudson Bay, but kept alive by building an igloo and eating one of their loved dog team.

In addition to their own son, now fifteen and away preparatory to starting school (there are no schools in these parts), they've acquired a little adopted eighteen-months-old Eskimo one. And you never saw anyone like him! The Leighs and everybody adore him. *I* love him to distraction. For the first time in my life, I believe, I know what it is to want a baby of my own — but not unless he can be like Donnie. His skin is pale brown, his cheeks dusky rose, his perfectly-shaped little head covered with a dark brown silky thatch. He has the most darling, laughing eyes I ever hope to see in any mortal. They're black and squint and turn up at the corners. He's sturdy and beautifully made and he *never* cries. He screws up his face when he falls but scarcely a whimper escapes him. Donnie love me too, for whenever he sees me he squints and dimples and holds out his arms. When I hug him he lies laughing up at me or listens to my watch tick with such enchanted sparkling eyes, I can scarcely tear myself away.

Here is the story of how the Leighs got him: An Eskimo, one Ookalik (this is also Eskimo for arctic hare), whom Mr. Leigh knew at one of his trading centers, had a part-white wife, who died tragically leaving her small baby. The winter before last Ookalik said to Mr. Leigh, "Your boy big. Now you got no baby. Maybe you like my baby?" Mr. Leigh, very busy at the moment, laughed offhandedly as whites are apt to do about a serious matter, said, "Sure I'll take him," and forgot about it.

A year later back at the same place again, along came Ookalik with a brown, fur-wrapped baby whom he handed to Mr. Leigh. "Here baby for you." Then perhaps sensing the surprise and consternation on the white man's countenance Ookalik reached out for the baby again. "Maybe you not want him now — I take him back. . . ."

But Mr. Leigh assured Ookalik that he did want him and carried him home to his wife.

"Imagine my feelings when Ed told me what he'd done! We'd wanted another baby, but a girl, and certainly not someone else's Eskimo one. . . .!"

"But," said I astonished, "do you mean to say you really *had* to take him?"

"I'd given my word, d' yu see?" said Mr. Leigh. "That means a lot to an Eskimo. Couldn't go back on it. If I didn't keep my word I wouldn't have any reputation with the brown faces. They know I don't go back on 'em once I've said something."

"Of course," said Mrs. Leigh. "There was nothing else to do —" *

The Leighs are a heartening pair. They're so contented and friendly. They've been through so much, faced life and death together so often in tough and lonely places. They have that quiet look in their eyes — a combination of poise and repose and far-seeing vision that strikes you forcibly after the feverishness and tortured mentality of great cities. They make a good marriage seem the wholly right and desirable thing, the nicest kind of companionship. After all, perhaps such couples are not so rare, simply because the ill-assorted kind, like objectionable tourists in Europe, are invariably the conspicuous ones.

How do the Leighs, for instance, feel about others of this world who don't live the highly regarded, respected life they do? I think the Leighs don't like certain aspects; for them it wouldn't do. But they're not greatly troubled by it. They don't judge something concerning the causes and circumstances of which they know little. They may not approve at all of a certain business or domestic arrangement, but they still can be warm friends, love kindness and selflessness, big heartedness

---

* Mr. and Mrs. A. A. Anderson, two of Churchill's best known citizens, who have lived in the North for many years and now own one of Churchill's largest stores, have a little Eskimo girl acquired in very much this same manner.

and courage; comprehend that to people such as these, the narrowness, bigotry, meanness, lack of real honesty which are part so often of the "respectable" world, are sins as great as ones for which they are condemned.

Only the other day Ronald recounted the story of a girl in Alaska where he once prospected. She'd taken her entire savings, earned at what a price for years, and given them outright to an old and ugly sourdough who had just lost his life's hoarding of gold in a wreck at sea. . . . And in the Yukon two more girls, tarts of the toughest, who, when everyone else was too terrified to go near him, kept guard alone all one night over a homicidal maniac; warmed and washed and fed him, so that the Mountie, taking him in without help some hundred miles to headquarters, could get direly needed sleep. What exactly are fineness and respectability anyhow?

But everyone up here is not wonderful, or intriguing, or lovable. The wife of one of the businessmen — a decent, nice-appearing sort of man too — arrived a while ago; a platinum blonde, more than usually good-looking. But underneath the beautiful blue eyes and the typical silvery hair and the baby complexion, and that extra sweet smile, there is apparently something more than disagreeable. Of course, it's centered around an abnormal yearning for men with all the accompaniments — an amazing and horrid variation of ways to attract, and so on — the sort of thing you don't really believe exists outside of books until you have to encounter it in real life.

I don't suppose the lady likes other women much anyway, but though we seldom encounter her (praise be!) she seems to have a special aversion to Sue and me and spreads unpleasant bits about us. The decent men dislike her, doubtless — but play up to her, outwardly at least, under the guise of gallantry or what not. This trait, in even the nicest of men sometimes, must be responsible for a lot of rotten female behavior. A flouting of convention, which is at least straight and open, seems far preferable to that which may be done under a cloak of respectable marriage.

But I suppose all these things, as well as the ways of someone like lovely Mrs. Leigh, here as well as elsewhere, form part of the truthful picture of life. And you wonder if it may not be a smaller, more open, better-proportioned part somehow in the big North than in the wholly conventional, outwardly respectable places of the earth?

The other evening Eric paid me a longer visit than usual. And he talked more than ever before about winters up on the Barrens.

The eastern side of the great Barrenlands, which extend roughly as far as Alaska and the Arctic Sea, begins just to the north of here and extends on up the west coast of Hudson Bay. This region is traveled over or trapped each winter by a number of these people. During the dark months of the year it must, quite literally, be one of the coldest and most desolate places on earth. No tree or hill, no change in landscape, nor any human sign except perhaps some trapper's tiny base completely drifted over, make the slightest landmark for any but the most experienced eye. In storms and the continuous semidark of the long winter months there is nothing. The flat or gently rolling ground, decorated with rock-hard, wind-tossed snow, merges imperceptibly into the treacherous sea ice of Hudson Bay.

The brief, unemotional, little tale Eric recounted of what living alone up there does to you inside, was the most gripping of all the fascinating and enthralling tales he's yet told me. There is the absolute terror that such isolation sometimes has for you. There are the things you face up to if accident or illness occurs or anything goes wrong, when the nearest other human being may be twenty or sixty miles away. During an arctic blizzard, even one mile off from another man may mean isolation as complete as if he were a hundred miles distant. In common with most trappers here, Eric and Ronald, though partners, each have their own trap lines and camps, and meet or travel together only part of the time. It's difficult for two men, however congenial, shut up together too long in a small space, not to get very dangerously on each other's nerves.

There is the story of what it means to be caught by yourself without adequate supplies miles from a camp or head base in an eighty-mile gale, completely blinding snow, a temperature of 60° or even 70° below. If you are wise, you have learned to build an Eskimo igloo of blocks cut out of firm drifts. This can stand up in gales and is stronger and warmer than a tent. A tiny primus stove or small seal oil lamp, such as Eskimos use, can keep the interior as warm as 40° or 60° above when arctic blizzards rage outside. The myriad crystals of snow walls throw back the beams of a single candle and light up gloriously the whole inside. An igloo may be built wherever there are banks of snow solid enough to be cut with a knife.

Usually snow is so hard in that region that a man can walk right on top of it, or else make out with very small, rounded snowshoes.

In late autumn once Eric and his dogs hunted caribou. The chase was exciting and they went so far they couldn't get back to camp before night. Then Eric went partly down through rotten ice and the covering of his legs and arms was soaked — the most hazardous

thing of all in temperatures of subzero. His matches
were wet, he couldn't make a fire, snow was too soft
for igloo building, there was absolutely no shelter. Suddenly a lone caribou appeared out of nowhere and he
shot it. He cut open the deer's stomach and thrust his
bare, already frozen hands and feet directly into the
hot, bloody inside (a trick learned from Indians one
time). And when he was warmed he skinned the animal and fashioned an imperfect but effectively warm
sleeping bag. He froze thin slices of meat (if you can't
cook meat, freezing is the next best way to render it
palatable), ate them, fed the dogs, greased his sled run-
ners with a bit of slippery sea mud to freeze hard overnight and make good traveling next day. So he made
out very well and passed a pretty good night after
all. . . .

With blizzards come the shrieking winds. "Some lads
just can't take the wind — it's not so much the ice cold-
ness of it, though God knows that's terrible enough, but
the unendingness of it — no letup for days and days.
Knew a chap went off his head about it. Used to scream
about the wind on a calm night when there wasn't a
breeze even — "

Last winter, trying to get back to his main shack,
Eric was caught in a blizzard near the coast. It was
the semidark of an arctic winter's day; in furious wind

and cutting, stinging snow he'd lost all sense of direction. Utterly done in and blinded he could barely stumble vaguely along, hanging to the handles of his dog sled. There was no physical strength left in him. The dogs, he was certain, were lost and traveling in the wrong direction. He began then to see a human figure which the dogs kept following. It would disappear for a time, then reappear again. It was the Spirit of Death, he thought, leading them to destruction. But still he was conscious enough to realize that he was nearly delirious from pain and cold and exhaustion; that to stop now would be to die. His five dogs, heads down in the lashing gale, thick fur completely snowed-over, were white ghosts struggling gallantly on and on (he never knew for how many miles or hours) pulling the load of traps and furs, until at last they bumped into something and stopped. The stovepipe of his own shack was sticking up through a rock-hard drift of snow.

As many and many a northerner has done before him, he owed his life to his dogs.

And part of course he owed to his own sheer grit and strength of character. These qualities above all else, I think, are what you sense continually in people of this world. They may be good or bad as I've said before, a mixture of both perhaps, but they're *strong*, not ever feeble or colorless.

And there is that other angle of life on the Barrens which Eric spoke of — even more forcefully and impressively, I thought, because it must be the things of the spirit and intellect and imagination which hold real men and bring them back, despite the hardness and terribleness, again and again. It's the beautiful part — the deep and satisfying contentment, the wonderful extra keenness of senses, that come from being completely self-sufficient; the absolute freedom of thought and action; the chance to see into the heart of things; the companionship of wild creatures and the sled dogs, so nearly akin to wild things themselves; the marvel of being so close to the earth, which is, after all, the best and true environment of all men. There is the sheer glory of a winterland, shades and shapes of snow, crystal nights of blazing stars. There are the fairylike periods of calm in a magic blue-white world when frost crystals and ice reflect moon or stars so brilliantly that you hardly know whether you're on earth or in the sky. There are the thrilling, tingling aliveness, and radiant color, of arctic auroras; all the attributes which are the very special living Spirits of the North, which only those who are hard enough and enduring enough are privileged to know.

"After you've been with a lot of buzzing people all summer," Eric said, "in the fall when you go out again,

it's just plain good to be alone. It's *wonderful* — unless
you get in a fix somehow — but even so you'd rather
risk it. Then if you meet up with your pardner or someone after being alone a few months, that's good too.
My God, how you talk — all night long without a stop
maybe — you dream out loud and talk about everything
you ever thought of — and argue — gosh! how you argue!"

The relationship between men who've been in such
a world together seems to mean something very special.
They often don't agree or approve of each other, yet
something like this exists between Ronnie and Eric.
There's much of it in the men up here. Perhaps it's the
reason why women, as such, seem mostly rather neg-
ligible in this world. It's not necessarily that they
aren't tough enough. It's just that any female, unless
she's a rather rare person, is really unimportant in the
general scheme.

I don't think Eric is able to speak of these things to
very many people. When he left he kissed me, dif-
ferently from any way I've ever been kissed before.
Except for a disconcerting habit occasionally, when he
says good-by, of ferociously holding your hand an unconventional length of time, Eric never touches you or
fools around. He said some lovely things to me which
are completely undeserved. But it's wonderful to have

someone even think you are the things you wish you might be; and care apparently so much for the very special qualities you'd love to possess.

Like most moderately attractive females I have been kissed before — in various circumstances by various sorts of men! Mostly I've absolutely loathed it and them; very occasionally it's been mildly nice. I thought descriptions of the marvelous effects of a kiss wildly exaggerated, or else that I'm just not the type. The wiseacres say you've never been kissed by the right man.

Of course I've no idea that Eric is the right man, or anything of that sort, but that kiss did something which nothing's ever quite done before. Maybe it's just because he is so forceful and compelling a person. I wish I knew. There are so many imponderables and unknowns about him. I think Bill would like him; for he's worth being interested in. Also Bill would say of course, "Watch your step" which, knowing that Eric's something very new to my ken, is precisely what I try continually to do.

I've no idea of what other men here say of Eric. They must respect his obvious capabilities, be interested in his vital personality. I doubt whether they disapprove of, or distrust, as people of our world would, his wanderings and completely independent habits. As he's hard to know, ruthless probably in some things, completely indifferent, I think, to opinions (he's often very rude to people he's not interested in), maybe they don't entirely like him either. I wouldn't know —

Ronnie says Eric's a woman hater — "mostly," with a grin at me. (I've always had an idea that this can mean too much experience with females rather than too little??)

Everyone likes Ronnie. He's always, outwardly at least, the most pleasant, obliging mortal. And he's got guts and strength and resourcefulness as well — he couldn't like the North if he hadn't. But sometimes there's a look in Terry's eye at its most penetrating, when he talks to the two men, which makes me feel he senses what I do (and I think Terry knows people): that if Eric were to put his force and ability toward something big and fine he'd be head and shoulders above Ronnie.

One night at supper Terry told us how Eric, during his first winter here, brought a sick Indian from fifty miles up the coast into Churchill. He had no dogs then to help and pulled the man most of the distance along rough sea ice on a tiny sled. "Took a lot of guts that did — Eric was new to this country, needed medical treatment 'bout as bad as the Indian did, time he got here. Kind of a fool thing to do — took a fool chance when he didn't know this ice. Indian wasn't much good either, though some of 'em are dandy fellows — but Eric found him alone and couldn't leave him — "

One thing this summer has shown me (that of course is one of the underlying reasons why I wanted to come away off up here even before I knew at all how wonderful it was) and that is that I can't marry Horace, fine and dear as he is. And if I'd stuck to our world and our kind of life, not seen anyone else who is important or viewed big horizons, that is exactly what I probably should have done. I'm beginning to appreciate Mother's terse advice (she's rather nice the way she's never burdened us with too many, too lengthy talks on the subject) that it's better not to marry anyone until you can't help it.

Eleven

∿∿∿∿∿∿∿∿∿∿∿∿∿∿∿∿∿∿∿∿∿∿∿∿∿

AUGUST 20TH. Last week one afternoon I strolled in leisurely fashion up to the Department House to get a geology book that Mr. Squire, one of the engineers, was lending me. Observing in the distance the *Fort Severn* being made ready to sail at an early date for Eskimo Point, I told Mr. Squire how terribly disappointed we were not to take that trip. He remarked then that Mr. Simpson, one of the head H. B. C. men come up on the last train, was at that moment in an office close by. Why didn't I stop, now, and ask him about it — just on the chance?

Feeling frightfully scared and shy without moral support from either Dr. C. or Sue, reminding myself sternly, "nothing ventured, nothing done," I started timidly forth, ran into Mr. Simpson on the spot, and then almost turned and ran out again. He was so very impassive and pale and tall. Presenting our case in a completely ineffective fashion, I was all set for the

[232]

refusal I knew was coming. No expression crossed his face; he reiterated, politely and icily, all the objections we'd heard before. I was about to get up and try to take a graceful departure when he suddenly smiled (*very* slightly), said that he'd heard of the interesting work we were doing, and added that "the Company" would like to help us out; if it were clearly understood we were going for the express purpose of scientific investigation, would not hold the Company responsible for accidents, and so on, why he could give us the necessary permission to sail on the *Severn*. . . . That is if we could get ready in time? She was due to sail that very evening — at 7 P.M. in fact. (It was then 5:30!)

Thanking him with all the warmth at my command, giving him ardent assurances on behalf of Dr. C. and Sue, promising to sign certain papers and pay our passage just before we got aboard, I departed sedately. And the minute I got outside started on a dead run for Sue's shack where, providentially, she was securely installed skinning specimens. Then she started on a dead run for the United Church and Dr. Carey.

Crimson and completely winded, I banged into the café and shouted between gasps, "Terry, quick, my shirt and socks!" (they'd been drying by the stove) to be met by the cold and scandalized stares of six strange tourists eating supper at the table. (It was the first time

anyone's ever been there at meals other than all of us
and the occasional trapper or railroad men.)

Twenty minutes later Sue hurtled in with a "Terry,
my pants!" to be met by the same six cold and scandalized stares. . . .

For one solid hour, Sue, Doc C, and I all *ran* between
café, tent, shack, stores and church, hurled things into
packs and duffels, panted and explained; and, assisted
with our loads by Ronnie and Eric whom we met most
opportunely on the way (Terry and Luke, snowed-
under by the unprecedented influx of tourists, hadn't
been any help at all), arrived at the H. B. dock at
exactly three minutes to seven.

We met Captain Douglas, a rather handsome, dark,
youngish man; and I introduced Dr. Carey and Sue to
Mr. Simpson. We all signed papers, said a fond farewell to Eric and Ronnie, and went impressively aboard
— to find the schooner wasn't going to sail for another
hour after all. Mr. Simpson had to show some visitors
around. . . . It was rather a relief, I think, to be leaving Mr. Grey's vicinity for a while and see him from a
distance, so to speak. Though he gave me one of those
infuriating parting looks which I shall remember probably to my dying day.

We had plenty of time to examine things and look
at the *Severn*. She was a lovely boat, I thought; a two-

master of about a hundred feet and seventy-five tons, freshly painted black, strong and solid and seaworthy with clean and graceful lines. Down below was a little cabin with three narrow bunks and a table; adjoining, was a tiny room belonging to the captain. Everything was trim and shining; there was an atmosphere of complete efficiency.

Trying not to get in anyone's way, for we felt privileged merely to be there, we then leaned on the deck railing, gazed at the evening, and waited.

Finally we sailed — across the river. To pick up the entire Indian camp which was to be transported fifty miles or so up the coast to the winter trapping grounds. This is a yearly accommodation of the H. B. C. which also helps them no doubt toward a good profit in furs.

But the whole camp, not having been notified — or not having properly understood — that it was to sail that night, was off fishing or away at church. The *Severn* had started with the Indians some days before and been forced back by high winds. Now the Indians weren't in any special hurry. The crew spent hours trying to round them all up. Then it was far too dark to pack and get underway. Our subarctic summer is practically over and dark autumn nights already are beginning.

All summer the brilliant colorful evenings, passing

imperceptibly into brilliant colorful dawns again, are so wonderful you almost forget the satisfaction of darkness and a sky at night. Here in this vast flat land, just as Bill describes it on the desert, one can truly see the stars and consider the universe.

We passed a disturbed night anchored out on the river. I put my sleeping bag on the tiny upper berth, Sue was below, and Dr. C. on a narrow settee just across from us — rather shocked, I believe, but enjoying himself. This life is doing him heaps of good. Not a word for ages of that mournful past.

In the morning there was Churchill — still on our right. The old scow sent to collect the Indians had sprung a leak, now the tide had gone out and left it on shore high and dry, the wind had come up again. . . .

We waited some more. Leaning idly over the side we chuckled grimly at the scramble which had practically reduced us to heart failures the night before. ("A land of infinite waiting, coupled with rapid, radical readjustment," Sue and I've decided, about sums up this world for us.) Neither captain nor crew, no one in fact, seemed at all perturbed about anything; and Dr. C., who had been in a great stew, was completely calmed down by now. This country is wonderful for "nerves."

Come to think of it, we haven't seen a newspaper (there is no such thing of course as a daily) or heard a radio all summer, although a few people apparently use them occasionally. Even if a war had started we're too remote here to do anything. Mostly there is unlimited time — except for silly scientists who want to find out everything in a month or two. If something isn't accomplished this year, it can be next, perhaps. Even vastly important trips and expeditions are dependent on seasons and weather. Man can't alter those, so he "waits on them" very philosophically —

A motor launch of people, newly arrived at Churchill by train and a small steamer just come in, stopped by the *Severn* and passed the time of day. They invited us to come aboard and go with them to see the old fort. Since we've had no chance to examine it except from a distance, and since Captain Douglas assured us that the schooner couldn't sail for hours yet, we gratefully accepted.

There were some quite fascinating characters aboard the launch — a missionary doctor and his young wife going to far-off Baffin Land, a couple come all the way from New Zealand en route to England, a journalist from remote countries of the east — Georgia, the Black Sea, Siberia. He was a most free and easy, exuberant American, but rather delightfully so. As we wandered about the grass-grown enclosure of the old fort walls, we got to be great friends and exchanged addresses.

There was a Swiss geologist, very famous (so he said), studying arctic and subarctic formations. He was extremely patronizing, so obnoxious that he was entertaining. For all his talk I'll wager Hudson Bay gives him a rough time.

Two miles up the river from the fort we stopped at Sloop's Cove, a lonely, tiny bay, which for two centuries formed a winter harbor for little trading vessels. On the ancient, lichen-covered, low rocks by the water's edge, were dozens of names and dates carved carefully and clearly by hand in solid stone two centuries ago (time doubtless hung appallingly heavy in those days), and great old iron rings to which the small stout ships had been anchored.

We returned finally to the *Severn* and a delicious supper cooked and served by Paddy, a charming Irish youth. Then at last the Indians began to come aboard — some thirty or forty — with babies and bundles (you couldn't distinguish one from another), baggage, sleds, tents, food, fifty dogs and puppies. The dogs, tied right together, roared as if they were killing each other. Babies screamed. Indians and dogs covered the deck three deep; some of the dogs were towed in the scow behind. You never heard such pandemonium.

Twenty-seven hours, exactly, after we'd first gotten aboard, the *Severn* sailed for open sea. The Indians and dogs were inland ones, mostly unused to water, scared to death and seasick.

There was quite a bit of motion, and my chief impression of that night on the tiny upper shelf was of starting up repeatedly out of a drugged sleep and banging my head a frightful whack on the ceiling a mere couple of feet above. This happened every single time Mr. Olson, the Swedish first mate, climbed down from deck and turned on a ceiling light by my head to consult the chart spread on the table. He wore a lavender parka and his fair hair and ruddy face, exactly like a huge Viking, loomed alarmingly close to mine. Each time he would say to me in a most distressed way, "I am so sorry!" and each time I would reply, "Oh, it's quite all right," subside, and fall asleep again instantly.

Early next morning, to the vast relief of everyone, Indians and dogs were disembarked, some to travel inland sixty miles or more to their trapping grounds.

We made a stop up the coast at Long Point to replenish a small supply base of the H. B. C. I went ashore with Mr. Olson and Mac, the Scots-Indian engineer, as dark as Mr. Olson is fair. I've never seen a better looking man than Mac; he seemed more Indian than Scot, and was as silent as Luke. But he had a flashing smile and appeared to be as capable as he was handsome. He's the most efficient engineer they've ever had, Mr. Olson said.

There was nothing at all at Long Point except a tiny well-built shack set completely alone on a wild and treeless shore. This was the supply base, a sort of emergency cache for anyone who needed to use it. There was a small, complete stock of all the necessaries plus a few luxuries: sacks of flour and oats, tobacco, coffee, tea, chocolate, sugar, dehydrated vegetables, matches, ammunition, wool underwear, socks, gloves, dog harness, caribou sleeping bags, parkas; even a dog sled, a canoe and outboard motor, aspirin and cough syrup, and a few books. There were oil lamps, a small stove, a supply of wood and coal.

On the high little counter lay a book containing names and lists of supplies taken by some trapper or lonely traveler. The place is not locked (very few places in the North are) and a man in need can go in and get what he wants, putting down his name, the date, and supplies he's taken. When he goes back to Churchill (it may be months or a year later), he goes into the H. B. Post and pays what he owes.

It was a very cold, dark day and Mr. Olson suggested that since I was probably the first white woman to honor Long Point with her presence, I should make the most of the luxuries it afforded and keep warm inside a caribou bag he spread out on the high counter, while he and Mac checked things over.

So, curled up in the coziest, most comfortable spot imaginable (no wonder caribou skin keeps you warm at 60° below), I looked over books or watched the two men seated just below. Funny marks and crosses were mixed in with supplies on the check list. These, Mr. Olson and Mac said, were made by such and such an Eskimo. They couldn't write down what they took but they would faithfully report it at some other H. B. Post — if not at Churchill, at Eskimo Point perhaps. They never cheated and they often left a fur or two right there which more than paid for what they'd taken. No, they had little trouble with anyone's cheating. People of the North mostly play square; and if they didn't it would be found out before long, for everyone knows everyone else. (The Company does seem to be so all-pervading and all-powerful, you wonder what profit there can be for any of these small independent traders? But I suppose they never attempt to deal, except in an unpretentious sort of way, with more than small, isolated areas.)

On a dark and empty sapphire sea we sailed northward again all day and the next night, up a wild, bleak, treeless coast (no more signs of the isolated fingers of forest which you see inland north of Churchill). There was little wind and engines were used most of the time. It was a perfect delight to be able to talk freely with each of the crew and acquire a firsthand knowledge of all parts of the boat. I'll never enjoy a big steamer again.

In the night we woke suddenly to stentorian shouts from the captain and mate on deck above us, shuddering stops and reversings, a sailor calling out constant reports of depth soundings. A big wind had blown up and we appeared to be in among dangerous reefs and shallows. Coming so unexpectedly in pitch dark it was rather terrifying. We had no real idea of what was going on and kept speculating as to when, and if, we were about to be wrecked.

But we got safely through into deep water again, and next morning reached Eskimo Point some hundred and sixty miles north of Churchill. Not so very far now — only about six and a half degrees — below the Arctic Circle! The schooner anchored some way out from the rough beach and we had to go ashore through sizable waves in a dinghy.

It was a very forbidding, desolate scene under a gray, angry sky. Completely treeless, the gray coastline and tundra rolled away from the inky sea and melted in purple distance. The summer season was over and fall had already begun. There was a subdued color over everything and a wild, sad charm. Howling dogs were scarcely distinguishable from shrieking gusts of the wind.

There were the Catholic and Anglican missions — two small churches with their respective houses, the small, white, red-roofed Hudson's Bay Post, a few tiny sheds, a big pole with the Company's flag flapping violently in the fierce, arctic breeze, and some twenty Eskimo tents of caribou skins or canvas. This, which was all there was of man in that vast wild land, was what we had traveled so far and worked so hard to reach.

Most of their year's supplies had come with us on the little black schooner, rocking away out there on the gray waves, now very small and blurred by mist and wind. The Catholic mission boat had already come and gone. Unless some odd dog team in winter travels as far south as Churchill, or some other unknown boat stops unexpectedly (this practically never happens) before freezeup begins, this was their last chance to send out mail and messages for another whole year.

Even as we landed, small boats and canoes full of Eskimos were helping the *Fort Severn* crew unload, and they looked to be having a rough time of it.

We met one of the Catholic priests, the H. B. man and his assistant, the Anglican missionary and his wife, Mr. and Mrs. Wilkie; all mildly — though only mildly, for one ceases to be surprised at anything in the North

— astonished to see a college professor and two American girls. The Wilkies invited us to spend the day with them and use their house as headquarters. Mrs. Wilkie was the only white woman at the settlement. With her auburn hair, fresh English face, and a lilting voice, she was darling.

The little white house to which she led us was amazing inside. A coal fire was burning in the tiny open fireplace of the small living room. There were paneled walls and several windows, many books, a few nice paintings, rugs, and easy chairs. There was even a bathroom (an unheard-of luxury in Churchill) with a bathtub and septic toilet. Though there was no running water, they could at least carry it in and immerse occasionally in a real hot bath.

We all had a thorough wash and Dr. C., to his joy, a shave. All of the house and its furnishings had been brought in piecemeal by boat over a course of years. It had taken some three years to assemble the bathroom. The bathtub arrived all by itself one August, the pipes and things to go with it appeared the next August, the toilet and wash bowl the year following.

Mrs. Wilkie took us to visit the Eskimo women in their tents. Like the Eskimos we'd seen at Churchill we were impressed again with how merry and friendly and contented they were. The mischievous grins on those plump brown faces and those twinkling black, little eyes were very fetching. They conversed happily in Eskimo with Mrs. Wilkie, who having been out here several years, was able to talk to them freely. Besides their own gay shawls and sealskin boots or caribou moccasins, they wore a comical assortment of white man's clothes in the style of 1910.

We spent some time in the tent of one plump little lady dressed in a trailing billowy cotton skirt and red sweater. Her most treasured possession was a hand sewing machine placed on the great thick bed of furs and clothing that completely covered the ground. Giggling and nodding, she knelt beside the machine and ran off seams at a violent rate.

It looked to be a lot easier and more fun than the sewing being done by two Eskimo ladies at the next tent we visited. One was making a pair of sealskin boots, the other the most luscious little fur rug from skins of unborn baby seals. They were a thick cream-white; they shone like silk and felt almost as good as velvet. The women were sewing with heavy steel needles (some still use needles made of bone or walrus tusk), threaded with the strong caribou sinews or fine muscles lying near the backbone of the animal. They alternately sewed and chewed the skins, for in order to have the skin soft and pliable enough to be shaped properly and receive a needle, it must be softened first by a thorough chewing.

There were beautiful things carved of walrus ivory: knives, and the handles of dog whips, whose flexible parts were of caribou hide plaited together. When Sue first arrived at Churchill at the end of May, people were still driving dog teams. It was fascinating, she says, to watch the skilled driver flourish these whips, some ten or twelve feet long, and hit precisely the right spot on any dog; or separate effectively a great fighting, roaring mass of fur into six or eight individual, moderately well-behaved canines. Once she saw an Indian neatly decapitate a ptarmigan with a single lash of his twelve-foot whip.

There were Eskimo ice goggles carved of walrus tusk. The two tiny elongated slits fitting over the eyes allow one to see quite efficiently, yet cut down light and glare so effectively that they are just as useful against snow blindness as any dark glasses. Long before the white man and his inventions came on the scene, Eskimos made out quite well with things of their own — perhaps in fact far better?

There were quantities of sled dogs about, some tied, some loose. One unspeakably patient bitch chained tightly to a driftwood log had six puppies pummeling and kicking and nursing at her belly.

All over the place little brown animals, a cross between a squirrel and small woodchuck, kept popping
up from holes. This was the Northern ground squirrel,
spermophile, or *shik-shik* as the Eskimos call it. Its
range doesn't extend as far south as Churchill.

Guillemots and seals were out on the water. On land
were Lapland longspurs and flocks of snow buntings.
We walked inland to look across the endless miles of
beautiful, bleak, gently rolling tundra. Small vales
were filled with white, billowy waves of cotton grass.
Late goldenrods were still in bloom, a northern species
of gentian, a wild flax. Prostrate willows, Vacciniums
beginning to turn bright red, cotton grass, Ledums, and
Rubus arcticus were common. But flowers and bird
life on the whole were rather scarce. It was too late in
the season. The blaze of summer blossoming Mrs. Wilkie said, had been over long ago. The autumn blaze
made of the scarlets, gold, maroon and russet, blue and
purple of the many kinds of little leaves and northern
berries, which in her eyes carpets the tundra as gor-
geously as summer flowers, was just beginning. It was
the first time I'd associated autumn colors with this arctic world and realized that they can be as thrillingly
beautiful spread densely over flat tundras as over trees
and woods and hills.

While Doc C. and Sue as usual were rushing about,

I stretched out by a sheltered hummock for a brief nap
— which, alas, I have become completely addicted to.
And Mrs. Wilkie promptly joined me with a pleased,
"Only fancy! Another sensible person!"

It didn't take long to see all there was of the settlement. Between gusts and misty showers we photographed Eskimo groups clustered about the store. Men
were coming and going with supplies from the *Severn*
— women and children were standing in groups. Most
of them seemed darker than those at Churchill, some
almost black. They had such very expressive, individual
faces. One buxom lady, tiny clay pipe sticking out from
an impish, utterly jolly round black countenance, rolled
her eyes at us.

It was too wet and blustery to stay out long and we
returned gratefully to Mrs. Wilkie's warm house and
the luxury of reading Masefield and Barrie in easy
chairs by the fire. Late in the afternoon Mr. Wilkie, an
intense, spiritual-looking sort of person, who like all
the men of Eskimo Point had been busy with boat-
loads, came in and we sat down to a feast: roast caribou, fresh Yorkshire pudding, tarts, after-dinner coffee.

In early evening when the wind had died somewhat
we were summoned to the *Severn*, now ready to sail
again. We said a warm good-by to the Wilkies and that
lovely little home in a far-off arctic land, and hurried

down to the beach. It was ticklish business trying to get out to the schooner. The sailors, waist-high in big breakers, tried again and again to shove our little boat off from shore and again and again we were hurled back. But finally we made it and climbed up and down over great, green waves.

Then it was impossible to board the schooner. Just as someone attempted to grasp the little ladder let down the side, a huge swell lifted the *Severn* high, completely out of reach, while our own tiny boat sank miles down in a huge black and green trough. It was the greatest fun. I was the first to get up the ladder at last, though I had to jump for it. But Doc C. and Sue were very solemn. After all, except for the Fox Island trip, this was their first experience at sea.

That night was pretty rough and we had to cling fast to our berths, but next morning it had cleared. There was still a strong breeze, all sails were up, and we went sweeping along gloriously through a blue and radiant world of crystal sky, warm sun, and tossing waves. Darling baby seals, little sea puppy dogs, kept popping up to turn backward flips and somersaults, there were a few eider ducks, scoters, and white whales.

"Nanook — off to starboard!" Rob, splicing rope, let out a great shout suddenly from the bow.

And there about a quarter of a mile away was a lone

white blob in the blue-green sea; not ice this time, but something we've been wild to see and never dreamed we should — a real live polar bear. The captain changed course a little and we got much closer; near enough to see the bear quite distinctly with glasses. You could just discern the small white head and long neck topping each swell with ease; sometimes the whole body appeared, a sort of phosphorescent green through the clear water. We were then some six miles out from land. But Mr. Olson has seen bears as far out as fifteen or twenty miles; feeding on seals and fish they follow the ice floes great distances. Those that come to land eat all sorts of vegetable matter, lichens and mosses, grass and berries.

We soon left the bear who was heading north, but the *Severn's* crew were all gathered about discussing it. Sometimes reaching a length of over nine feet and weighing occasionally as much as sixteen hundred pounds, Nanook (the Eskimo title is far more common all over the North than the English "polar bear") is said by some observers to be almost, if not, as big as the great Alaska brown bear. Its lovely thick white fur is greatly prized; the man who kills Nanook, be he white or Eskimo, is a great hunter, for hunting polar bears may be a risky pastime. Unless very hungry or deliberately molested, however, Nanook in common with most wild animals, does not bother man and does its best to avoid him. The bear is a wonderful swimmer and completely at home in water; on land it runs swiftly; its sight and sense of smell are remarkably keen. Apparently it is a quite common animal around Southampton Island.

None of the crew seemed to be agreed as to the hibernating habits of polar bears, though all said a pregnant female invariably hibernates. In some snowed-over crevice of ice or deep tunnel, usually two young are born about January. They're less than a foot long and weigh scarcely two pounds, though their mother may be a seven or eight hundred pounder. In March, when sun begins to get high again, females and young cubs can be seen hunting food far out on the sea ice. Captain Douglas told us that "krill," composed of little sea organisms in pools on the ice, forms food for fish. Seals come after the fish, the polar bears in turn after the seals.

By that time I'd gotten to know the very efficient crew from Captain Douglas and Mr. Olson to the sailors, Rob and Sig, an Icelander, Mac and Paddy. Each one was interesting and a real individual. I would have loved to have sailed with them and talked with them for weeks. The wonderful air and exhilarating motion gave me a stupendous appetite. But the appetites of my poor Sue and Dr. C. fell off alarmingly. They refused to come down to meals at all and stayed on deck, clinging palely to the rails at every sweep and swerve. Though as far as I know they were never actually sick.

Captain Douglas and I ate three huge meals in solitary state and got to know each other quite well. I hadn't realized anything connected with such a far-off land could produce such food; one meal included roast turkey, cranberry sauce, and lemon pie. He was most reserved but once started, exceedingly interesting. Before he began to work for the H. B. C. he must have sailed all the seven seas. This summer's job at Churchill is more or less of a temporary one and he hopes to be sent farther north where he's lived before. He was quite astonishingly intellectual — intellect deepened and balanced by knowledge of life and experience. But then as I've said before one ceases to be amazed at anything one meets with up here.

We discussed in particular the problem of missionary and Eskimo; how confusing it must be in a tiny place like Eskimo Point for the Eskimo to be urged by two separate sets of white people to worship our God and carry on the Christian religion in a quite different manner. I thought the medical care, lessons in clean living, consideration of the individual such as I gathered the

Wilkies are trying to instill, was the most valuable. But of even this angle Captain Douglas was doubtful. Why, he asked, should we wish to change the brown faces when on the whole they are already such gentle, harmless, useful, contented sort of people? When they have a definite culture and religion of their own based on life in a land which they know and have happily survived in for generations? Their customs, he said, grow out of economic necessity; the way they must live to keep their healthy standard and survive successfully. And from the unbelievable hardness of their environment has come a remarkable nobility of character which enables them, without bitterness, to face up to reality, no matter how terrible that reality may be. For example, where there is little or no contact with white civilization and its attending ills, it is the custom for aged people who have become a dangerous drag on their community, to wander deliberately far out onto the snow or ice, freeze, and die. Babies, mentally or physically deficient, usually are destroyed. When an Eskimo's wife falls ill and is unable to accompany him on a hunting trip, another Eskimo, without reservations, loans his wife for the time being. If the trip is a long and important one, a woman is needed vitally to provide comfort and keep camp for the men, sew and prepare fresh skins for the making of garments.

Then the white missionary comes to tell them these things are evil. For his part Captain Douglas thinks it more than tragic that so few missions apparently can give the Eskimo the benefits of Christianity and literacy without also taking from them their unique ability to adjust themselves happily and profitably to a forbidding land.

At this juncture a great lunge of the schooner sent dishes sliding off the table and a milk pitcher upset. The dignified captain looked seriously annoyed and his dissertation on the missionary field was brought to an abrupt termination.

But just as enthralling, I thought, as his talks on Eskimos and missions were tales of encounters with animals of the North — in particular the walrus. Once in a motor boat with Eskimos not far from Southampton Island, he landed suddenly in the midst of a huge herd. In no time at all regular prehistoric monsters with great, hideous, wrinkled faces, little blood-shot eyes, and huge tusks appeared above water and completely surrounded the small launch. There were horrible grunts and terrible, mighty roars. It was the most gruesome sight and sound; he'd never been more terrified in his life. He knew of instances where Eskimos out hunting walrus had their boats upset when a walrus hooked its tusks over the side. Only two years ago an Eskimo he'd once traveled with was crushed to death and pounded to pulp by the huge tusks.

These tusks, which are elongated upper canines, sometimes up to thirty-nine inches long, though used in fighting, are fashioned especially for digging clams and other sea forms off bottom when the walrus submerges. The tusks prevent the walrus from using its front teeth to tear bits of food, but there are pads covered with thick, short, very coarse bristles, on either side of the walrus's muzzle, which serve as extra lips and efficient forks and knives.

The walrus is ten to twelve feet long and weighs as much as two thousand or three thousand pounds. It's a most valuable animal to the Eskimo, not only for the beautiful ivory tusks, but also for the great, thick, rough hide used for all sorts of things from dog harness to roof coverings, and the huge quantity of meat that just one big body provides for both men and sled dogs. Left alone to live its own life and uninterfered with, again like nearly all the "fiercest" animals, it is harmless to man.

The walrus extends pretty much over arctic seas; it is found in northern Hudson Bay and on some of the islands here. But it's been hunted far too extensively and is such a gregarious animal it's easy to kill. In many places it has been seriously depleted or completely exterminated. When the animals are crowded together like a flock of sheep by the dozen or hundred upon ice floes, it's a simple matter for men to get close to them and in a cruel and completely unscrupulous manner, mow them down with high-powered rifles.

Once Captain Douglas saw a dozen walrus clambering upon an ice floe already crowded to the brim with some two dozen others. The ice floe, top-heavy suddenly from extra tons of new arrivals, tipped promptly into the sea; the cursing and the pandemonium among the walrus crowd was something to remember.

After that wonderful sail all one night and one day and part of another night, over an empty sea on which ours was the only boat, we returned to Churchill. That night around 2 A.M., our masts black against a star-studded sky, like a ghost ship creeping into a ghost harbor devoid of life, we entered the Churchill River.

Two of the *Severn's* crew offered to help us home with our packs. Rob, who on his broad back carried my heavy one to my tent doorstep, received the fright of his life when Nero, son of a wolf, leapt at us in the dark. Nero recognized me instantly for he licked my hand and followed me into the tent. But he growled deeply when I shook hands with Rob to say a warm good-by and try to thank him. I wish that dog were mine.

There is not much time left now before we have to go out on the train; it's a rather desolate thought. Don't see how I shall bear up under the loads of conventions and cultures of the civilized life. Father Pierre has gone off on his last long trip before snow sets in, and I shall not be able to tell him how I've passed up my one chance to "miss the boat" and study an arctic winter.

Twelve

∿∿∿∿∿∿∿∿∿∿∿∿∿∿∿∿∿∿∿∿∿∿∿

Augusт 28тн. This is being written on the train from
Churchill to The Pas. It will be another week or two
perhaps before we reach home since we're to stop over
in Winnipeg to look up material for Dr. Stevens and
visit people who've worked on the north country. So,
while they're still fresh in my mind, I want to speak of
the last few days at Churchill.

There was great excitement after we got back from
Eskimo Point. Five small steamers from Europe came
in for grain and supplies. Several carried passengers.
One, with the Premier of Manitoba aboard, had been
stuck in ice in the middle of Hudson Bay for over a
week. There were extra freight trains bringing in grain
and, in addition to the regularly weekly one, a large
tourist train. Churchill has seethed with sudden activity.

Dr. C. gave a talk to a packed audience in the little
United Church. In the back row Sue and I sat beside

an Indian family — father and mother, baby, two children. They were all most dignified. All were clad in the usual wool trousers or skirts, sweaters, and scarves. Each of them, including the baby, wore caribou moccasins and rubbers. Every so often Papa emphatically blew his nose on a huge, red handkerchief, after which the handkerchief always passed right down the line and each member of the family followed suit. . . . It's depressing to be returning to a world where such cheering things never happen.

The last day was spent in frantic packing of specimens — plants and bird skins and egg sets galore, clothes and materials, making last minute preparations and farewell visits to special people: my darling little Eskimo, Mrs. Leigh, and Mrs. Taylor. Somehow these two are not dissimilar despite the different pattern of their lives. Both have that inner strength, a sort of innate decency, a very wonderful kindness.

There was a last walk on the rocks in a wild and stormy sunset, a last listening to the Music of the North: arctic winds on the tundra, weird cries of the old-squaws, splashing of whales and seals, the singing of the husky dogs. I can't help thinking I shall see and hear it all again some day.

On our last night there was a dance in the large storage building, used also for a recreation hall, up toward the docks. All summer we've been pressed earnestly by various members of Churchill's male population to attend the regular weekly one. But we were away usually on some trip; and the dances sounded so rough we were a bit scared off. However, we decided this would be a good one to attend by way of fulfilling social obligations — and we did want to sample at least one.

It *was* an experience! The tourists helped greatly to swell the female population, but still there weren't quite enough ladies to go around. Every single person, male or female, that we'd ever seen around Churchill was there. Sue and I, very literally, were rushed off our feet. Ronnie and Eric did their best (Doc Carey wouldn't attend) and cut in at every opportunity, but some of the men just wouldn't be cut in on. More than once they practically came to blows — shook fists and nearly pushed each other down. I've never felt so wildly popular in my life. We danced with all the *Severn's* crew except the captain, who was probably too dignified to attend, every man, I think, we'd ever encountered around Hudson Bay, and quantities we'd never seen.

Sue even danced with Manitoba's Premier. Terry's a marvelous dancer ("See what ye girls have been missing not coming to the dance all summer?") There were all sorts of partners from those who held you gaspingly close in a bear grip (most alarming!) so you couldn't breathe or move your feet, to those who at arm's length pushed you about like a sack of potatoes. Some were polished men of the world, some regular hulking ruffians.

They had all kinds of dances — not just modern ones but delightful exhilarating waltzes and wild highland flings. By about 1 A.M. Sue and I were so completely done in that Eric and Ronnie had to take us home.

Eric and I had a farewell talk lasting for hours. He told me some surprising things. He's probably going to take a government job having to do with a geographical survey which will take him north and west to the Mackenzie and Coppermine River territories. After the wonderful free life of the last few years on the Barrens, he doesn't know whether he can stick such work. But financially at least, he believes there's little future in trapping. Besides he has a distaste more and more for injuring animals which he likes. Ronnie doesn't know what he may be doing next year — possibly he will return to Scotland and the old family place and sheep raising. They may first do one more season of trapping together depending on the date of Eric's new job.

Eric wants me to marry him some day. And, whether the government job turns out or not, he will come down next year to take me "back to the North." He takes it completely for granted that he will do this! Bill's so understanding, he will guess what this summer has done to me. Though he's over thirty, he's steered unusually clear, I think, of serious entanglements. I don't think Bill's ever been very deeply stirred by anyone. Or, if he has he's certainly kept it under his hat. But if for the first time in his life he were, I wonder what he'd do? Would he pass it up, even if it were something of an unknown quantity?

Many of our family have contributed much to the world and honestly helped those less fortunate. But they themselves have been too sheltered, too naïve, too utterly unacquainted with people outside their own small spheres. Even those beloved relatives whose wisdom we've been trained to revere, refuse actually to recognize so many evil circumstances of life. We've been rather instilled with the idea that these are "unreal," "sensational," something which "happily we know doesn't exist." It's been our attitude about plays or books, or types of behavior we don't like, that hurt our tastes or sensibilities or ideals.

Grandfather was always quoting, "There is no sin so great as ignorance." But what he meant was ignorance of book-learning, the sciences, cultural and intellectual things — not ignorance of character and customs and behavior of which he disapproved.

For a long time I've sensed dimly that all this wouldn't quite do for me. Now I'm sure it won't. I have to experience wider, bigger things. I have to know more, though sometimes it must be far easier and safer and pleasanter not to know, to believe in the best, have little to do with the hard and the sordid and the ugly. But *knowledge* of such things doesn't necessarily have to hurt a mature person, does it? Perhaps this is what maturity means.

Can one help to bring about peace and brotherhood (such a creed of our family) unless one really knows other types of people, bad or good, congenial or otherwise, their ways and minds and problems?

Although there's still so much about Eric of an unknown quantity, somehow I've ceased to be greatly concerned and become imbued, I think, with that northern attitude of taking human beings for what they are here and now. If he comes for me (and I think somehow that he will), maybe I'll have to chance it. Perhaps if I do I shall lose out, experience great unhappiness. But I've done just enough mountain climbing to be aware that to know the real heights you must also know the depths. To know great things, you must have great courage, take a great risk. And I want to try, at least, to know the great things. . . .

It's just as well these dissertations — far more voluminous than I ever dreamed they'd be — have to end at last. So much seems to have happened in so short a time.

References

ALLEN, ARTHUR A. "Birds of Timberline and Tundra," *National Geographic* (Washington, D. C.) (September 1946).

ANTHONY, H. E. *Field Book of North American Mammals.* New York: G. P. Putnam's Sons, 1928.

BAUMGARTNER, A. MARGUERITE. "Private Secretary to a Tree Sparrow," *Bird Lore* (May-June 1936).

——. "Nesting Habits of the Tree Sparrow at Churchill, Man.," *Bird Banding* (July 1937).

BAUMGARTNER, FREDERICK M. "New Birds for Churchill, Man.," *The Auk* (April 1936).

BECKETT, EVA. "Plant Life of the Churchill District," *Canadian Geographical Journal* (Ottawa), (August 1945).

——. "Our Historic Northern Route," *Canadian Geographical Journal* (March 1941).

——. "Whales Give Oil and Meat," *Family Herald and Weekly Star* (Montreal), (April 20, 1949).

——. "Fruitful Barrens," *Family Herald and Weekly Star* (May 5, 1948).

CAHALANE, VICTOR H. *Mammals of North America.* New York: Macmillan Co., 1947.

[265]

GRAY, ASA. *Gray's New Manual of Botany*, 7th ed. New York: American Book Co., 1908.

PETERSON, ROGER TORY. *A Field Guide to the Birds.* Boston: Houghton Mifflin Co., 1947.

SUTTON, GEORGE MIKSCH *and* HAMILTON, WILLIAM J., JR. "The Mammals of Southampton Island." *Memoirs of Carnegie Museum*, Vol. XII. Part II, Section 1. Pittsburgh: 1932.

TAVERNER, PERCY A. and SUTTON, GEORGE MIKSCH. "The Birds of Churchill, Manitoba." Reprint from *Annals of Carnegie Museum*, Vol. XXIII. Pittsburgh: May, 1934.